Masers and Lasers: Physics and Design

Masers and Lasers:
Physics and Design

J. S. Thorp

Department of Applied Physics, University of Durham

Macmillan
London · Melbourne · Toronto
St Martin's Press
New York

MACMILLAN AND COMPANY LIMITED
Little Essex Street London WC2
also Bombay Calcutta Madras Melbourne

THE MACMILLAN COMPANY OF CANADA LIMITED
70 Bond Street Toronto 2

ST MARTIN'S PRESS INC.
175 Fifth Avenue New York NY 10010

First published 1967

Demy 8vo, viii + 312 pages
157 line and 14 half tone illustrations

Printed in Great Britain by Richard Clay (The Chaucer Press), Ltd.,
Bungay, Suffolk

Contents

✳ This symbol indicates sections and chapters more suitable for post-graduate reading.

* This symbol indicates sections and chapters more suitable for post-graduate reading.

Preface

MASERS and lasers have developed in a remarkably short space of time from being new discoveries to acquiring a reputation as well-established devices. Moreover, their uses in many fields of application are becoming steadily more important in everyday life and this emphasizes the need for a widespread appreciation and understanding of them. This book has three main objectives. Firstly, to give an account of the essentials of masers and lasers suitable for undergraduate study. Secondly, to provide for the post-graduate student a bridge between elementary accounts and the detailed specific texts and original papers, and thirdly, to present for qualified scientists and engineers engaged in research and development a survey of masers and lasers covering a fairly wide field.

The sixteen chapters are grouped into three broad divisions covering masers, lasers and the science of maser and laser materials. Chapters and Sections which require a fairly wide background knowledge of physics are marked with an asterisk to indicate that they are more suitable for post-graduate reading. The main Chapters give references for further detailed study and a short list of books suitable for supplementary background reading is included at the end of the book.

In order to keep to a reasonable length attention has been confined to the essential principles of masers and lasers. The book will have achieved its purpose if it engenders a desire to learn more about them. It is a pleasure to acknowledge the encouragement, advice and assistance which have been so readily given by numerous people both here and elsewhere during the preparation of the manuscript.

J. S. THORP
Department of Applied Physics
University of Durham

1

Stimulated Emission

T H E words *maser* and *laser* were practically unknown a decade ago. Nowadays, however, both are firmly established in scientific language and we may reasonably enquire about their origin. The name maser, derived from the initial letters of the words in the phrase *microwave amplification by stimulated emission of radiation*, is used to describe any device which amplifies signals at microwave frequencies by using the quantum mechanical principles of stimulated emission. The stimulated radiation is coherent, and maser amplifiers are characterized by their very low noise temperatures as compared with conventional microwave amplifiers. More generally the term *maser action* is used to signify any process by which coherent stimulated radiation is obtained after the normal population distribution of an energy level system has been disturbed.

Shortly after the successful operation of microwave maser amplifiers corresponding experiments on stimulated emission were made at optical frequencies. These resulted in the generation of coherent light beams and the devices, again quantum mechanical in nature, were called lasers, standing for *light amplification by stimulated emission of radiation*. The term *optical maser* is sometimes used instead of laser. Both masers and lasers can be used either as amplifiers or oscillators and in the general title we do not usually specify exactly which is intended. However, at microwave frequencies we are more often concerned with the amplification whereas at infra-red and optical frequencies we are more interested in the generation of radiation.

From the physical point of view one of the most exciting features of masers and lasers is that they demonstrate how stimulated emission of radiation, predicted theoretically by Einstein (1.1) in 1917, can be achieved in practice. As a result of this many experiments concerning the nature of coherent light, which were previously not feasible, are now made possible because beams of adequate intensity are available. Added incentive in the subject was given at an early stage by the application of masers as frequency standards and low noise amplifiers in microwave communication systems and radio-astronomy. The applications of lasers, already exceedingly numerous, form a very rapidly expanding section of the scientific literature.

1.1 Absorption of radiation

One of the first problems is to understand something of the nature of stimulated emission and to do this the interaction between an electromagnetic wave and a collection of atoms must be considered. At this stage there is no need to specify in detail the kind of atoms which are actually used. Later Chapters show that suitable arrangements can be found in gases, solids and liquids. At the moment it is only necessary to assume that the atoms may exist in a variety of energy states and that, for convenience, they are contained in an enclosure. To simplify the analysis imagine that the atoms may exist only in a lower energy state E_1 or one of higher energy E_2. Transitions between these two states may then be caused by an incident electromagnetic wave whose frequency ν_0 is given by

$$h\nu_0 = E_2 - E_1 \qquad (1.1)$$

where h is Planck's constant. This resonance condition is illustrated in Fig. 1.1. Equation (1.1) is familiar from its occurrence in optical and X-ray spectroscopy and it is, of course, of very general application. However, as a consequence of the Uncertainty Principle, the energy levels cannot be perfectly sharp and hence the frequency of the transition cannot be perfectly monochromatic; a very narrow band of frequencies thus satisfies the resonance condition.

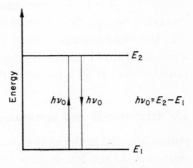

FIG. 1.1 The resonance condition for transitions between two energy states

If the system is in thermal equilibrium the number of atoms in each energy state will be constant. The transition from the lower to the upper energy state can occur in only one way, namely by the absorption of a photon of energy from the radiation field. At

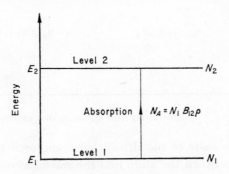

FIG. 1.2 The absorption process

resonance the number of atoms per second excited to the upper state is proportional to the number N_1 present in the lower state, the radiation density ρ and the probability B_{12} of an

3

absorption occurring per second. We may write for the absorption process

$$N_A = N_1 B_{12} \rho \qquad (1.2)$$

where N_A stands for the number of atoms absorbing per second. The situation is represented diagrammatically in Fig. 1.2: the absorption of a photon from the wave causes an upward transition between level 1 and level 2 thus increasing the population of level 2 above its thermal equilibrium value.

1.2 Stimulated and spontaneous emission

Atoms already in the upper energy state can make a radiative transition to the lower state by one of two alternative ways, Fig. 1.3. The first of these is by stimulated emission and we can obtain a qualitative picture of the process by recalling the

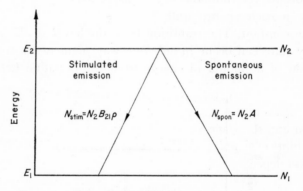

FIG. 1.3   Stimulated and spontaneous emission

classical behaviour of the driven harmonic oscillator. In the interaction between the atom and the wave the motion of the bound electrons is perturbed. If the phase of the incident wave is such as to oppose the electron motion the atom will lose energy, emitting a photon. In a collection of atoms all those experiencing this phase relation will be affected in the same manner, and so all of them will emit photons at the same instant. This represents the stimulated emission of coherent radiation. Under resonance conditions, i.e. when the frequency of the incident wave corresponds exactly to the frequency of the transition given by equation (1.1), the photons produced by stimulated emission have the same frequency as the incident wave. In other words amplification of the incident radiation occurs.

The number of atoms producing stimulated emission per second N_{stim} is given by the relation

$$N_{stim} = N_2 B_{21} \rho \qquad (1.3)$$

where N_2 is the number of atoms in the upper energy state, B_{21} is the probability for a stimulated transition from the upper to the lower energy state and, as before, ρ is the radiation density. It is worth noticing the similarity between equations (1.2) and (1.3) and especially that both N_A and N_{stim} are proportional to the radiation density, i.e. to the strength of the incident electromagnetic wave.

The second way in which an atom in the upper state may emit a photon and fall to the lower state is by spontaneous emission, which corresponds classically to radiation damping. Here there is no phase relationship between the electron motion and the wave and so the emission is incoherent. The probability of an atom in the upper state emitting spontaneously does not depend on the strength of the incident wave. Thus the number of atoms N_{spon} undergoing spontaneous emission per second is

$$N_{spon} = N_2 A \qquad (1.4)$$

where A is the transition probability for spontaneous emission.

1.3 The Einstein coefficients

We can now combine equations (1.2), (1.3) and (1.4) bearing in mind the assumption that the collection of atoms is enclosed

5

and in thermal equilibrium. The number of atoms absorbing radiation must equal the total number emitting radiation, i.e.

$$N_A = N_{\text{stim}} + N_{\text{spon}}$$

and so

$$N_1 B_{12}\rho = N_2 B_{21}\rho + N_2 A \qquad (1.5)$$

The transition probabilities B_{12} and B_{21} for upward and downward transitions have so far been distinguished. However, since the phase of the incident wave determines whether absorption or emission will be obtained and each phase is equally probable, these are equal and hence

$$B_{12} = B_{21} = B \qquad (1.6)$$

The quantities A and B are known as the Einstein coefficients. They can be related to each other either by comparison with the Planck radiation law or more rigorously by quantum mechanical analysis (1.2). The ratio B/A is a very important parameter because it represents the ratio of stimulated to spontaneous emission from the atomic system. Since the coherent stimulated emission corresponds to amplification at the signal frequency and the incoherent spontaneous emission represents noise, the ratio B/A gives a measure of the signal-to-noise ratio obtainable from the system.

Equation (1.5) can be rewritten as an expression for ρ, the radiation density, giving

$$\rho(N_1 - N_2)B = N_2 A$$

or

$$\rho = \frac{1}{(N_1/N_2 - 1)} \frac{A}{B} \qquad (1.7)$$

The Planck radiation law gives for the radiant energy density $\rho(\nu)$ at frequency ν

$$\rho(\nu) = \frac{8\pi h}{\lambda^3} \frac{1}{\exp(h\nu/kT) - 1} \qquad (1.8)$$

where the wavelength λ is c/ν and k is Boltzmann's constant. It is now necessary to introduce a result which follows from the original assumption that the atomic system is in thermal

6

equilibrium. The distribution of atoms between the upper and lower energy states is governed by Maxwell–Boltzmann statistics and in thermal equilibrium at a temperature T

$$\frac{N_2}{N_1} = \exp\left(-\frac{h\nu}{kT}\right) \qquad (1.9)$$

This relation is extremely important in understanding laser and maser operation and its implications are considered later. For the present purpose, however, it is sufficient simply to use the value for N_1/N_2 obtained from equation (1.9) to substitute in equation (1.7) and so obtain

$$\rho = \frac{1}{\exp\left(h\nu/kT\right) - 1} \frac{A}{B} \qquad (1.10)$$

We can now compare coefficients in equations (1.8) and (1.10). This gives

$$\frac{A}{B} = \frac{8\pi h}{\lambda^3} \qquad (1.11)$$

This relation shows that the ratio of spontaneous to stimulated emission varies as the inverse cube of the wavelength of the radiation. We should remember moreover that the value of h is $6\cdot62 \times 10^{-27}$ erg second and so we can see that in the microwave region, where $\lambda \sim 1$ cm, spontaneous emission is almost negligible compared with stimulated emission. In the optical region, however, the wavelength is much shorter, e.g. $\lambda \sim 5000$ Å, so the noise contribution due to spontaneous emission is increased by a factor approaching 10^{13}. As appears later it is in the microwave region that low noise amplification can be obtained. In the optical region the interest is chiefly in obtaining intense coherent light beams.

It is useful to have the exact values of the separate Einstein coefficients and the results of the quantum mechanical calculations will be quoted without giving detailed proofs (see 1.2). The value of the coefficient A for spontaneous emission is

$$A = \frac{64\pi^4}{3h\lambda^3} |\mu^2| \qquad (1.12)$$

where $| \mu^2 |$ is the square of the matrix element for the transition, to which reference is made later. The corresponding expression for the coefficient B, representing the transition probability for stimulated emission, is

$$B = \frac{8\pi^3}{3h^2} | \mu^2 | \qquad (1.13)$$

This gives the probability of stimulated emission per second per unit radiation density. When particular examples for the atom system are taken equation (1.12) enables the approximate number of photons emitted spontaneously per second to be derived. If the transitions involve electric dipoles this procedure shows that at one centimetre wavelengths the probability of spontaneous emission from the upper state to the lower is of the order of 10^{-7} per second. If the transition involves magnetic dipoles the probability is reduced to about 10^{-11} per second because the matrix element for magnetic dipole transitions is much smaller than for electric dipole transitions.

1.4 Population inversion and noise

As already pointed out the spontaneous emission represents noise in a maser amplifier and the equations derived above can be reconsidered from the point of view of finding the conditions under which coherent low noise amplification may be obtained in practice. The noise contribution N_{spon} is determined simply by N_2, the number of atoms in the upper energy level, and A, the transition probability for spontaneous emission whose value will be constant for the particular atomic system chosen.

On the other hand there are two ways in which N_{stim}, the number of photons produced by stimulated emission, may be increased. The first is to increase the value of ρ, the radiation density of the electromagnetic wave acting on the system. This can be achieved, depending on the frequency of operation, by containing the collection of atoms in a microwave resonant cavity or an optical resonator. The second method is to increase the value of N_2. This alternative creates a more fundamental difficulty because, as equation (1.9) shows, N_2 is always less than N_1 for a system in thermal equilibrium at any finite temperature. Therefore the number of photons absorbed will always exceed the number produced by stimulated emission. Thus to make a maser operate the normal population distribution across the signal levels must be altered so as to make N_2 greater than N_1. This process is often called population in-

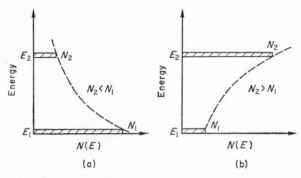

FIG. 1.4   Population distributions in a two-level system (a) in thermal equilibrium, (b) with population inversion

version and succeeding Chapters show how this state can be achieved in a variety of atomic systems. Fig. 1.4 illustrates the difference between a two-level system in thermal equilibrium and one in which an inverted population has been established. We may notice in passing that in a two-level system we can at best only equalize the populations in the two levels by simply applying a steady electromagnetic field to the system.

It has already been pointed out that the signal-to-noise ratio of the maser will be determined by the ratio of stimulated to spontaneous emission obtained. By enclosing the atomic system in a resonator and so increasing the density of the radiation field the latter ratio can be made large, giving the possibility of very low noise amplification. The ratio N_{stim}/N_{spon} does not directly involve the physical temperature T of the system. This means that it should be possible to make amplifiers whose equivalent noise temperatures are below the physical temperatures of the atomic systems and are limited only by the minimum spontaneous emission obtainable. Equation (1.11) also shows that the ratio A/B is inversely proportional to the cube of the wavelength of the radiation. At optical wavelengths the spontaneous emission is much greater in proportion to the stimulated emission than at microwave wavelengths. Thus in the microwave region the chief interest is in the low noise amplification properties of masers whereas in the optical region much of the interest centres on the use of lasers as oscillators producing intense coherent beams rather than as amplifiers in the former sense.

References

1.1   EINSTEIN, A.: *Phys. Z.*, 1917, **18**, p. 121.
1.2   SINGER, J. R.: *Masers* (Wiley, 1959).

2

The Ammonia Maser

THE ammonia maser was the first device to operate successfully using the principle of stimulated emission of radiation
(Gordon, Zeiger and Townes, 2.1, 2.2). This uses a beam of
ammonia molecules as the active material and in this respect
differs from the other types of maser which will be described
later. It provides, however, a particularly direct method of
obtaining an inverted population and also illustrates many of
the features which arise in other types of microwave maser.
This Chapter first outlines the general arrangement of the
ammonia maser and then describes in more detail some of the
design problems and performance characteristics.

2.1 General principles

The energy levels used in the ammonia maser are vibrational
states of the ammonia molecule. In the most usual form of the
molecule the three hydrogen atoms lie at the corners of a
triangle, Fig. 2.1, and the nitrogen atom can vibrate along a line
perpendicular to the plane of the hydrogen atoms, thus occupy-
ing sites such as 1 and 2. We can imagine that the hydrogen
atoms rotate while the nitrogen atom oscillates between two
positions above and below the plane of the hydrogen atoms.

These two structural arrangements do not represent exactly the same energy for the molecule because the wave functions for the hydrogen and nitrogen atoms are not quite symmetrical. We may thus speak of the molecule being able to exist in two energy states. There are in fact many possible

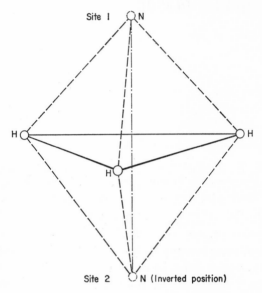

Site I ○N

H○ ────────────── ○H

H○

Site 2 ○ N (Inverted position)

FIG. 2.1 The ammonia molecule

vibrational states, but the two which are of interest for maser applications are those whose energy difference corresponds to a microwave frequency of 23·87 kMc/s. Fortunately these also have the strongest vibrational transition. The resulting resonance line has a very narrow width.

A schematic diagram of the ammonia maser is shown in Fig. 2.2. A beam of ammonia molecules emerges, as in molecular beam techniques, from an aperture in an oven whose temperature can be closely controlled. The beam, containing at this stage molecules in both the upper and lower energy states, then passes through an electrostatic separator. Separation of the energy states can be effected by a non-uniform electric field because the electric quadrupole moments of molecules in the upper and lower energy states are different. Thus in a given field gradient the deflections of the two types of molecules are different and two separate beams are produced. It is usually arranged that the upper state molecules continue to move along the axis of the system while the lower energy state molecules escape sideways. By careful design of the separator it is possible

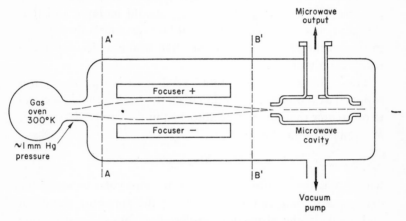

FIG. 2.2   Schematic diagram of the ammonia maser

not only to separate the molecules but also to focus the upper state molecules into a well-defined beam. Thus between the planes marked AA′ and BB′ in Fig. 2.2 population inversion is obtained by direct physical separation, and in the plane marked BB′ the beam consists almost entirely of molecules in the upper energy state. These then pass into a microwave resonant cavity whose resonant frequency is carefully adjusted to that of the ammonia vibrational transition, 23·83 kMc/s. The cavity has a very high Q and so there is a sufficient noise power level to initiate emission from the upper state molecules which then revert to the lower energy state and emerge from the cavity. Provided that sufficient upper state molecules arrive continuous oscillation can be maintained and the output may be taken from the waveguide coupled to the cavity; alternatively, the system may be operated just below the oscillation regime as a continuous reflection type cavity maser amplifier.

We can see from this outline that several important considerations enter into the design of the maser and that the detailed construction of the apparatus is by no means as simple as Fig. 2.2 might imply. It is clearly desirable that there should be as many upper state molecules as possible entering the cavity per second, that the Q of the cavity should be large and that the cavity resonant frequency should be very carefully adjusted to that of the ammonia resonance line whose molecular bandwidth is only about 4 kc/s.

The condition for continuous oscillation is that the power supplied as stimulated radiation from the beam should be equal to or greater than the power absorbed in the cavity. The power P supplied by the beam is

$$P = Nh\nu_0 \mid a \mid^2 \qquad (2.1)$$

where N is the number of upper state molecules entering the cavity per second, ν_0 the frequency of the ammonia transition and $\mid a \mid^2$ is the transition probability for an upper state molecule to revert to the lower state. (As the beam consists almost entirely of upper state molecules on entering the cavity $\mid a \mid^2$ is initially zero and increases as the molecules traverse the length of the cavity.) The power P_L lost by absorption in the cavity walls is simply

$$P_L = \frac{\omega_0 W}{Q} \qquad (2.2)$$

where Q is the cavity quality factor, W the energy stored in the cavity and $\omega_0 = 2\pi\nu_0$. Thus the condition for oscillation, which states that these two quantities should be equal, means that

$$Nh\nu_0 \mid a \mid^2 = \frac{\omega_0 W}{Q} = \frac{\nu_0 \epsilon_1^2 V}{4Q} \qquad (2.3)$$

where V is the cavity volume and ϵ_1 is the amplitude of the electric vector of the r.f. field in the cavity. If the time t taken for a molecule to traverse the cavity is small and the r.f. field strength in the cavity is not too large the approximate expression

$$| a |^2 = \left(\frac{\pi \mu \epsilon_1 t}{h} \right)^2 \qquad (2.4)$$

may be used to give the value of the transition probability at resonance (Singer, 2.3). (μ is the electric dipole moment.) Inserting this value of $| a |^2$ into equation (2.3) gives for the minimum number of molecules per second required to maintain oscillation

$$N = \frac{hV}{4\pi^2\mu^2 t^2 Q} \qquad (2.5)$$

In terms of the cavity length L and cross-sectional area A this can be rewritten as

$$N = \frac{hv^2 A}{4\pi^2\mu^2 L Q} \qquad (2.6)$$

where v is the average molecular velocity. The mean molecular velocity is of course controlled by the oven temperature and kinetic theory gives the relation as

$$v^2 = \frac{4kT}{m} \qquad (2.7)$$

where m is the mass of the molecule and T is the oven temperature. At $T = 300°K$ the value of v is about 10^5 cm/s and with realistic values for Q, L and A the magnitude of N is about 10^{13} molecules per second. It turns out that with some of the special focusing separators which have been developed these flux requirements can be achieved without undue difficulty.

Not all of the power emitted by the ammonia molecules in the cavity can be extracted as a useful power output from the maser. Some is used up in overcoming cavity losses and the proportion of the remainder which emerges from the coupling iris depends on the Q value of the iris. If the useful power output is P_o and the Q-factor for the output coupling is Q_1

$$P_o = \frac{\omega_0 W}{Q_1} \qquad (2.8)$$

where as before W is the energy stored in the resonant cavity. The optimum value of Q_1 has been shown to be about twice the loaded Q of the cavity and Gordon, Zeiger and Townes have estimated that the maximum available power output will be of the order of

$$(P_o)_{\text{max}} \simeq \tfrac{1}{2} N h \nu_0 \qquad (2.9)$$

In practice the output power levels of ammonia masers are restricted to about 10^{-9} watts because of the limitations on availability of high flux beams of upper state molecules.

2.2 Separator and cavity design

As mentioned above the lower and upper state molecules can be separated by passing the beam emerging from the oven through a non-uniform electric field. When the ammonia molecule is placed in an electric field the distribution of charge in the molecule is altered and a dipole moment is induced. This dipole moment then interacts with the electric field. The internal energy of an upper state molecule is increased and that of a lower state molecule is decreased so that, in a non-uniform electric field, lower state molecules will move towards the higher field region and conversely the upper state molecules will move to the lower field region.

The separator arrangements used by Gordon, Zeiger and Townes are sketched in Fig. 2.3. In the first arrangement four hollow metal rods each 22 in long were placed round the beam with an inter-rod spacing of 0·080 in and d.c. voltages of 15 kV were applied as shown. In the second arrangement six rods 8 in long were used at a spacing of 0·16 in with 30 kV

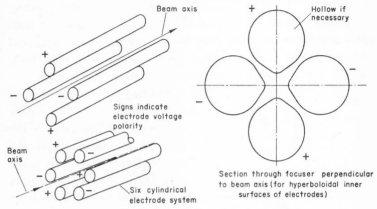

FIG. 2.3   Axial rod focusing separators

applied. In both arrangements the inner faces of the focusing electrodes were shaped as hyperbolas — to enable the field gradients to be calculated exactly — and the second configura-

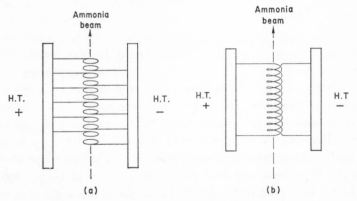

FIG. 2.4   Ring- and screw-focusing separators

tion was found to give higher field gradients and better efficiency. More recently ring and screw focusers have been developed. These have the forms shown in Fig. 2.4 and behave as lenses for upper state molecules. The advantages of the ring and screw focusers are that the units can be smaller than rod systems and that better efficiencies can be obtained. Comparisons of different focusing systems made under corresponding conditions (Becker, 2.4) showed that the efficiencies of both ring- and screw-focusing units were between about 90% and 95%, whereas a six-pole rod type focuser was only 60% efficient and a four-pole rod focuser about 40% efficient.

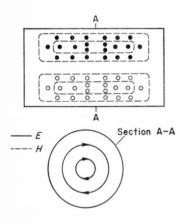

FIG. 2.5   Field pattern in the H_{011} cylindrical mode

Turning to consider some of the essential points in cavity design the analysis given of the method of operation of the maser shows that each molecule should spend a reasonably long time in the cavity in order to maximize the probability of stimulated emission occurring. In practical terms this means that the cavity should have a long length relative to its cross-sectional area and for this reason cylindrical cavities are often used. In other words, the factor QL/A, appearing in equation (2.6), is a sensitivity factor and should be large in order to minimize the beam flux required. In Gordon, Zeiger and Townes' maser resonant cavities made of copper and silver-plated invar were used. These were about 4·5 in in length and had internal diameters of 0·6 in. They were operated in the H_{011} mode and gave unloaded Q values of $Q_0 \simeq 1200$. The r.f. field pattern for the H_{011} cylindrical mode is shown in Fig. 2·5. The beam entered the cavity through a coupling hole 0·4 in diameter and the cavity was tuned by a precision plunger at the other end.

A detailed analysis of cavity design for ammonia masers was

made by Shimoda, Wang and Townes (2.5) who defined a figure of merit M for a cavity as

$$M = \frac{LQ_0}{A}\left(\frac{8}{\pi^2}\right)^n \qquad (2.10)$$

where Q_0 is the unloaded cavity Q, and the index n has the value of $n = 0$ for a zero axial mode and $n = 1$ for a unity axial mode. They then calculated values of the parameter $(\mu_s \delta M)$ —

Table 2.1

Mode	Radius (a cm)	Narrow beam ($\mu_s \delta M$)	Broad beam ($\mu_s \delta M$)	Unloaded Q (Q_0)
H_{111} (TE_{111})	0·37	12·2	5·9	6 100
E_{010} (TM_{010})	0·48	28·4	7·7	10 800
E_{011} (TM_{011})	0·48	22·2	6·0	10 400
H_{211} (TE_{211})	0·61	0	2·9	8 100
H_{011} (TE_{011})	0·76	0	4·1	17 800

Properties of cylindrical cavity resonators with $L = 12$ cm and $\lambda = 1·25$ cm

the product of the specific permeability μ_s, the skin depth δ and the figure of merit — for various modes in cylindrical cavities. One of the sets of results is given in Table 2.1. From this we can see that the E_{010} mode has a higher figure of merit than the H_{011} mode used by Gordon, Zeiger and Townes and in fact it required only about one-third of the molecular flux for operation. The r.f. field pattern for the E_{010} mode is shown in Fig. 2.6. The mode should be chosen so that the directions of the r.f. field components ensure the maximum transition probability for stimulated emission.

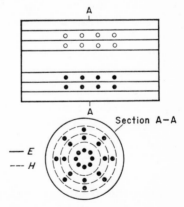

FIG. 2.6   Field pattern in the E_{010} mode

2.3 Maser performance

The ammonia maser is rather exceptional in that it is more suitable as a very narrow band oscillator than as a general purpose microwave amplifier although it has been used in special circumstances for the latter purpose. The reason for this lies in the very narrow bandwidth which can be obtained with the ammonia maser oscillator. As we have seen the total molecular bandwidth, $2\Delta\nu_B$, of the resonance line (i.e. the full width at half the peak intensity) is itself quite small, being only about 4 kc/s. In the maser oscillator, however, very appreciable narrowing can occur as a result of regeneration in the cavity and the amount of narrowing increases with increasing power output. Under oscillating conditions the total linewidth $2\Delta\nu$ at half-peak intensity is related to the molecular bandwidth by the expression

$$2\Delta\nu = \frac{8\pi k T (\Delta\nu_B)^2}{P_B} \qquad (2.11)$$

where P_B is the power emitted from the ammonia beam and T is the absolute temperature of the cavity. Masers such as those described above give output powers of about 10^{-10} watt and so with the cavity at room temperature the oscillator linewidth is reduced to about 10^{-2} cycles per second. This very narrow linewidth is ideal for a frequency standard (Townes, 2.6), and represents an equivalent Q for the ammonia maser of about 5×10^{12}. This same feature, however, tends to restrict the use of the ammonia maser as a low noise amplifier because usually much larger bandwidths — about 1 Mc/s in some communication systems — are required.

The frequency stability of the ammonia maser is very important when it is used as a frequency standard. This is influenced by a number of factors and has been considered in detail by several authors (e.g. 2.5, 2.6 and 2.7). The most important factor causing frequency fluctuations is temperature instability of the cavity since any change in the cavity dimensions immediately produces a change in its resonant frequency. Other factors involved include frequency pulling between the cavity and the molecular oscillator system, the slight variations in dielectric constant of the molecular beam in the cavity due to changes in the number of molecules entering the cavity and, to a lesser extent, Stark and Zeeman shifts in the frequency of the molecular resonance due to stray electric and magnetic fields. With silver-plated invar cavities maintained at constant temperature, however, stabilities of 1 part in 10^{10} over one hour have been achieved.

The discussion in Chapter 1 showed that the primary importance of the microwave maser lay in its potential as a low noise amplifier. The ammonia maser enabled the first tests of this theory to be made. The methods of measuring maser noise properties are rather complex (Helmer, 2.8, Alsop, Giordmaine, Townes and Wang, 2.9), and here reference will be made simply to the results obtained at a very early stage in the growth of masers. The experimental measurements were in reasonable agreement with theory and proved conclusively that low maser effective noise temperatures could be obtained. Gordon and White (2.10) cooled the cavity of an ammonia maser in liquid nitrogen and obtained a maser noise temperature of about 75°K. The comparison between this figure and the corresponding value of about 3000°K for a good quality conventional superheterodyne receiver at the same frequency is very striking.

References

2.1 GORDON, J. P., ZEIGER, H. J. and TOWNES, C. H.:
   Phys. Rev., 1954, **95**, p. 284.
2.2 GORDON, J. P., ZEIGER, H. J. and TOWNES, C. H.:
   Phys. Rev., 1955, **99**, p. 1264.
2.3 SINGER, J. R.: *Masers* (Wiley, 1959), p. 25 et seq.

2.4 BECKER, G.: *Quantum Electronics III* (Columbia University Press, 1964), p. 393.

2.5 SHIMODA, K., WANG, T. C. and TOWNES, C. H.: *Phys. Rev.*, 1956, **L02**, p. 1308.

2.6 TOWNES, C. H.: *Suppl. del Nuovo Cimento*, 1957, **V**, Serie X, p. 1.

2.7 HELMER, J. C.: *J. Appl. Phys.*, 1957, **28**, p. 212.

2.8 HELMER, J. C.: *Phys. Rev.*, 1957 G, **107**, p. 902 (L).

2.9 ALSOP, L., GIORDMAINE, J., TOWNES, C. H. and WANG, T. C.: *Phys. Rev.*, 1957, **107**, p. 1450 (L).

2.10 GORDON, J. P. and WHITE, L. D.: *Proc. I.R.E.*, 1958, **46**, p. 1588.

3

Population Inversion at Microwave Frequencies

In the first two Chapters we have seen that in order to obtain maser action the normal thermal equilibrium population distribution across the signal levels must be altered so as to obtain an excess population in the upper energy state. The ammonia maser represented a two-level system in which, since the active material was a molecular beam, a high excess population in the upper state could be obtained by the physical separation of molecules. The same principle has been used in other molecular beam masers, e.g. the hydrogen maser (3.1), but generally speaking it is not of wide application. It is in solid materials, particularly paramagnetic single crystals, that energy level systems having energy differences appropriate for microwave transitions are found. This Chapter has two main objectives, firstly, to explore the energy level systems available in paramagnetic single crystals, and secondly, to show how inverted populations may be obtained in them. The initial discussion concerns paramagnetic solids. These were, apart from ammonia, the first materials in which maser action was observed and they have also subsequently proved very useful for solid state lasers. The following sections describe methods of obtaining inverted populations in these materials, particularly the three-level method of operation proposed by Bloembergen (3.2) for continuous maser operation, and mention some of the problems which arise from relaxation effects. Throughout this Chapter the discussion will be confined to outlining the physical processes involved in population inversion. Later Chapters give detailed accounts of the experimental methods by which population inversion is actually achieved.

3.1 Energy levels in paramagnetic single crystals

(a) *Energy level diagrams*

The design and performance of a maser are very closely dependent on the material used and so one of the first questions we must ask is which materials have energy levels appropriate for the wavelengths to be amplified. The latter lie in the microwave region, i.e. in the centimetric or millimetric range, and of these any corresponding to wavelengths used in communication or radar systems will be particularly important. A large number of masers utilize the electron spin levels provided by the spectra of paramagnetic single crystals and we will examine some of these.

A widely used material is ruby, i.e. single crystal α-alumina in which a small percentage of the aluminium atoms have been replaced by chromium. The chromium, whose concentration is kept down to about 0.05% for reasons which are given later, enters the lattice in the triply ionized state giving Cr^{3+} in Al_2O_3. (There are in fact two positions in the unit cell at which the chromium atom may be located but these are equivalent sites.) Chromium is one of the ions of the iron group in which the paramagnetism arises from electrons in the unfilled $3d$ shell and the ground state of the free Cr^{3+} ion is ⁴F. When the chromium ion is situated in a single crystal, as, for example, in salts such as the sulphates, nitrates and alums and in the refractory oxide host lattices, the internal crystalline electric field is sufficient to quench the orbital angular momentum, and the paramagnetic behaviour is due to electron spin only. For the Cr^{3+} ion the effective spin value is $S = 3/2$.

Aluminium oxide has trigonal symmetry and the internal crystalline electric field has components of both cubic and trigonal symmetry. The cubic component removes some of the

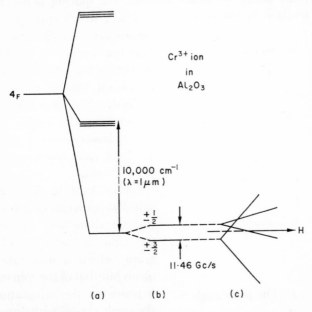

FIG. 3.1 Energy level diagram for ruby showing (a) splitting of orbital levels by a crystal field of cubic symmetry, (b) partial removal of spin degeneracy of lowest orbital level by crystalline non-cubic field and spin-orbit coupling and (c) Zeeman splitting of ground state levels in a magnetic field

degeneracy of the ground state of the free ion, Fig. 3.1, and gives a spectrum with a singlet ground state and two orbital triplets, the lower of which is removed from the ground state by about 10^4 cm^{-1}. The lower symmetry components of the crystalline field cause a further splitting of the ground state and two levels are produced which are separated in energy by about

0.5 cm^{-1}. Each of these two levels still has spin degeneracy which is unaffected by the crystalline electric field. Thus, if the crystal is placed in an external magnetic field, the spin degeneracy can be removed and we get Zeeman splitting of the two levels giving, in the case of Cr^{3+}, four spin states. The important points to notice are that the spacing between the spin levels is of the order of 0.5 cm^{-1}, which corresponds to microwave wavelengths, and that the frequency at which a particular transition occurs depends on the magnetic field applied. (We may notice in passing that the higher orbital energy levels are those involved for laser transitions at optical wavelengths.)

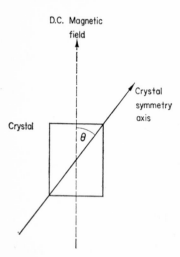

FIG. 3.2 The polar angle θ

Closer examination of the spin levels reveals that because the crystalline field acts on the Cr^{3+} ion the energy level diagram (which is now taken to mean just that of the spin states) depends on the orientation of the single crystal with respect to external magnetic field. To clarify matters the polar angle θ is defined as the angle between a prominent crystal axis and the magnetic field, Fig. 3.2. In ruby the trigonal axis, the c-axis, is taken as the prominent axis. Thus any particular energy level system must be referred to its corresponding polar angle. The effect of polar angle is quite marked, as we can see from Figs. 3.3 and 3.4, and so if a particular frequency and transition are to be matched there are two variable parameters available, the polar angle θ and the strength of the d.c. magnetic field H.

If the normal selection rule for transitions between spin states is applied only first-order transitions having $\Delta S = \pm 1$ are allowed; strictly, other transitions are forbidden. Fortunately, however, as a result of the crystalline electric field and residual spin-orbit coupling, the energy levels are not pure spin states. Therefore the normally forbidden $\Delta S = \pm 2$ and $\Delta S = \pm 3$ transitions are in fact observable although their intensities are

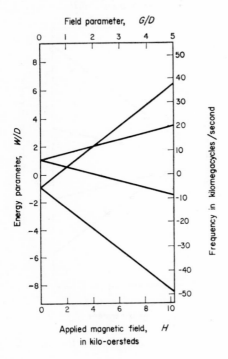

FIG. 3.3   Energy level diagram for ruby, $\theta = 0°$

much lower than those of the first-order transitions. This 'mixing of states' is a fundamental requirement in c.w. maser operation and is discussed more fully later. Because of the mixing of states it is not normally possible to allocate to each energy level a single spin quantum number applicable at all fields and polar angles. The nomenclature used in Figs. 3.3 and 3.4 is that suggested by Schultz–du Bois (3.3), but sequential

27

numbering starting from the lowest energy state is also commonly used.

Many other paramagnetic crystals have been used or suggested as maser materials. All of these materials are mag-

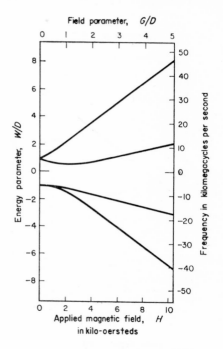

FIG. 3.4   Energy level diagram for ruby, $\theta = 90°$

netically dilute, i.e. the concentration of the required paramagnetic ion is sufficiently low to ensure that direct spin–spin interaction between neighbouring paramagnetic ions is small. Some of them are listed in Table 3.1. The first to be used successfully in a maser was gadolinium ethyl sulphate (Scovil, Feher and Seidel, 3.4). Here the gadolinium ion has a spin of $S = 7/2$ giving a spectrum of eight levels (shown diagrammatically in Fig. 3.5) in which, with a field of $H = 2850$

oersteds and a polar angle of $\theta = 90°$, the signal transition across the $-5/2$ to $-3/2$ levels occurs at 9 kMc/s. Chromium-doped potassium cobalticyanide also has a useful energy level system for centimetric wavelengths, Fig. 3.6, and also has a

Table 3.1

Maser material		Effective spin	No. of levels
Phosphorus-doped silicon	P-doped Si	$\frac{1}{2}$	2
Irradiated calcite	$CaCO_3$	$\frac{1}{2}$	2
Irradiated quartz	SiO_2	$\frac{1}{2}$	2
Irradiated magnesium oxide	MgO	$\frac{1}{2}$	2
Gadolinium/lanthanum ethyl sulphate	$Gd/La(C_2H_5SO_4)_3.9H_2O$	$\frac{7}{2}$	8
Potassium chromi-cobalticyanide	$K_3Cr/Co(CN)_6$	$\frac{3}{2}$	4
Ruby	Cr^{3+} in Al_2O_3	$\frac{3}{2}$	4
Sapphire	Fe^{3+} in Al_2O_3	$\frac{5}{2}$	6
Chromium rutile	Cr^{3+} in TiO_2	$\frac{3}{2}$	4 *
Iron rutile	Fe^{3+} in TiO_2	$\frac{5}{2}$	6 *

Some maser materials
(* Two non-equivalent sites per unit cell)

single paramagnetic ion per unit cell (McWhorter and Meyer, 3.5). Chromium-doped rutile, however (Gerritsen, Harrison, Lewis and Wittke, 3.6), is a material where there are two non-equivalent sites in the unit cell. Thus there is a composite energy level diagram containing the states due to each chromium site separately except at particular polar angles, determined by the crystallographic symmetry of the unit cell, where the levels

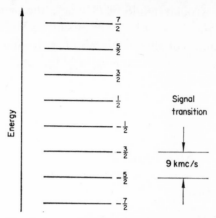

FIG. 3.5 Sketch of energy levels of gadolinium ethyl sulphate at $\theta = 90°$, $H = 2850$ oersteds, showing the signal transition at 9 kMc/s

overlap. We can see from these examples that, purely from the point of view of finding a material with appropriate energy level spacings, there is a considerable freedom of choice of materials.

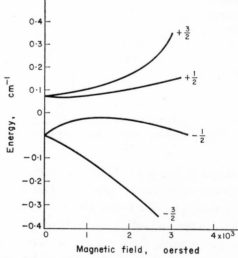

FIG. 3.6 Energy level diagram for potassium chromi-cobalticyanide, $\theta = 0°$

However, this is not the only criterion for a successful maser material and some other aspects of the question are considered later.

✳ (b) The spin Hamiltonian

The usual way of presenting information regarding the energy level system of an ion in a paramagnetic single crystal is by means of the *spin Hamiltonian* $\mathcal{H}_s$. The general Hamiltonian $\mathcal{H}$ for a paramagnetic ion in a single crystal may be expressed in the form

$$\mathcal{H} = \mathcal{H}_0 + \mathcal{H}_c + \lambda'LS + \beta(L + 2S)H \qquad (3.1)$$

and gives the energy of the system. In equation (3.1) the term $\mathcal{H}_0$ is the Hamiltonian for the free ion and $\mathcal{H}_c$ gives the interaction with the crystalline electric field. The third term, $\lambda'LS$, in which λ' is a constant and L and S are the operators of the total orbital and spin angular momenta respectively, represents spin-orbit interaction. The last term is the one in which we are most interested. It represents the interaction of the spin system with the magnetic field H and has the form $\beta(L + 2S)H$, where β is the Bohr magneton,

i.e.
$$\beta = \frac{e\hbar}{2mc} \qquad (3.2)$$

In setting up a Hamiltonian similar to equation (3.1) it is assumed that dipolar and exchange interactions between neighbouring ions are negligible — this holds for magnetically dilute single crystals. The relative importance of the various terms in the Hamiltonian depends on the nature of the paramagnetic material considered. For example, in a salt of the iron group, in which the magnetism arises from the unfilled $3d$ electron shell which is strongly exposed to the crystalline field, the term for crystalline field interaction will predominate. The orbital angular momenta are quenched and thus the ground state is left with only a spin degeneracy of $(2S + 1)$.

In the rare-earth salts on the other hand the magnetism arises from the $4f$ electron shell which is well screened from the crystalline electric field because it lies near the core of the atom. In this case spin-orbit interaction is the predominant effect and the ground state has a degeneracy of $(2J + 1)$. Generally speaking, many of the iron group salts possess cubic symmetry whereas those of the rare earth elements have lower symmetry.

In maser operation we are primarily concerned with the spin states and so may use an abbreviated form of Hamiltonian — the spin Hamiltonian $\mathscr{H}_S$ — corresponding to the last term of equation (3.1). The spin Hamiltonian is an expression for the energy of the spin system and is built up by adding together successive terms representing modifications to the basic Zeeman splitting of the levels. It may be written as

$$\mathscr{H}_S = g\mu_B HS + D[S_z^2 - \tfrac{1}{3}S(S + 1)] + E[S_x^2 - S_y^2] \quad (3.3)$$

where the parameters D and E, which are tensors, represent the cubic and trigonal components of the crystalline electric field (Bleaney and Stevens, 3.7, Bowers and Owen, 3.8). Equation (3.3) neglects the terms for interaction with nuclear spins — giving hyperfine spectra — and higher powers of the spin operators. The eigenvalues representing the energy states are found by operating on the spin state with the spin Hamiltonian and diagonalizing the matrix so obtained.

In the special case of some cubic crystals both the parameters D and E may be equal to zero. More often masers use materials such as gadolinium ethyl sulphate or ruby where the paramagnetic ion is situated in a crystalline field having axial symmetry, and here $\mathscr{H}_S$ must contain a term involving D. This parameter determines the spacing of the spin levels and, as we can see from Fig. 3.3, the energy difference between the spin levels in zero magnetic field (the zero field splitting) is $2D$. In axially symmetric crystals the parameter E is zero and the anisotropic Landé splitting factor g can be described by only two components, one $g_{//}$ parallel to the symmetry axis and the other $g_\perp$ perpendicular to it. Normally the symmetry axis is taken as the z-direction. Taking, as an example, the case of Cr^{3+} in Al_2O_3, the effective spin is $S = 3/2$ and the symmetry of the crystal field leads to $E = 0$. With the magnetic field along the z-axis the spin Hamiltonian becomes

$$\mathscr{H}_S = g_z\mu_B H_z S_z + D[S_z^2 - \tfrac{5}{4}] \qquad (3.4)$$

and there are four spin levels separated at zero magnetic field by $2D$. In maser crystals of lower symmetry we must retain the term involving E in the spin Hamiltonian. An important result of this is that the spin states differing by $\Delta S_z = \pm 2$ are mixed and so $\Delta S_z = 0$ transitions are allowed, with a transition probability proportional to $[E/g\mu_B H]^2$, when the d.c. and r.f. magnetic fields are parallel. The parameters in the spin Hamiltonian are found from experimental measurements, D being obtained directly from the zero field splitting and the g value from the magnitude of the magnetic field at resonance. In materials which are used for masers the linewidths of the transitions between the spin levels are usually between about 15 and 30 oersteds — the reasons for this are discussed in subsequent sections.

✳ 3.2 Two-level inversion

In solid materials it is of course not possible to separate individual spins spatially in any scheme analogous to that used in the ammonia maser. It is, however, possible to invert the populations of two levels which may either be selected from the multi-level systems we have been considering or, more simply, by the Zeeman levels of a crystal having an effective spin of $S = \tfrac{1}{2}$ such as phosphorus doped silicon, a material used by Combrisson, Honig and Townes (3.9) in early maser experiments, irradiated calcite, irradiated magnesium oxide or some of the nickel salts. The methods for obtaining inverted populations in two-level systems are rather complicated. Three

33

techniques have been suggested, field reversal, the 180° pulse, and adiabatic rapid passage, of which the last appears most promising. A description of these techniques is deferred until Chapter 5 partly because of their complexity and more particularly for the reasons which follow.

If a two-level system is used as an amplifier, operation will proceed in two stages. The first stage must be to establish an inverted population, and only when this has been achieved is the system in a suitable state to give stimulated emission, i.e. to amplify an incoming signal. The generation of photons by stimulated emission naturally reduces the number of spins in the upper energy state — which is also depleted by simultaneous spin-lattice relaxation — and so the inverted population rapidly disappears as a normal thermal equilibrium distribution of population is restored. The inversion process must then be repeated before the spin system can amplify again. Thus a two-level maser must, by the nature of its operation, be a pulsed amplifier. In most microwave systems where maser amplifiers would be useful, e.g. in communication systems, a major requirement is for the amplifier to operate continuously and because of this most interest centres on the c.w. masers which operate on the principles we shall now describe.

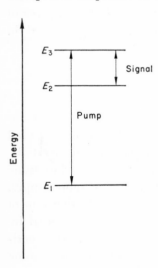

FIG. 3.7 Three-level maser operation

3.3 Three-level maser operation

A scheme for continuously maintaining an inverted population across spin levels was proposed in 1956 by Bloembergen (3.2). Suppose we consider three of the energy levels of a multi-level spin system, Fig. 3.7. In thermal equilibrium at some

34

temperature T the populations of levels 3 and 2 will be given by Maxwell–Boltzmann statistics as

$$N_3 = N_1 \exp\left[-(E_3 - E_1)/kT\right] \qquad (3.5)$$

and
$$N_2 = N_1 \exp\left[-(E_2 - E_1)/kT\right] \qquad (3.6)$$

where N_1 is the population of level 1. If the energy differences are small compared with kT we may take the first terms in the expansions of the exponentials and write

$$N_3 = N_1 - N_1 \frac{(E_3 - E_1)}{kT} \qquad (3.7)$$

and
$$N_2 = N_1 - N_1 \frac{(E_2 - E_1)}{kT} \qquad (3.8)$$

These approximations are reasonably valid for centimetric wavelengths and helium temperatures. The difference in population between levels 1 and 3 is then

$$N_3 - N_1 = N_1 \frac{(E_3 - E_1)}{kT} \qquad (3.9)$$

Suppose microwave radiation of frequency ν_p — the pump frequency — is applied to the crystal such that

$$E_3 - E_1 = h\nu_p \qquad (3.10)$$

At resonance absorption will take place and, if the pumping power level is sufficiently great, levels 3 and 1 will be saturated so that their populations are equalized. Let the new populations in the three levels after pumping be n_1, n_2 and n_3. Referring to the uppermost level, the population will have been increased by half the difference in the initial populations of levels 1 and 3, while that of the lowest will have been reduced by the same amount. Thus

$$n_3 = n_1 \qquad (3.11)$$

$$n_3 = N_3 + \tfrac{1}{2}N_1 \frac{(E_3 - E_1)}{kT} \qquad (3.12)$$

and
$$n_1 = N_1 - \tfrac{1}{2}N_1 \frac{(E_3 - E_1)}{kT} \qquad (3.13)$$

35

We must now refer back to Fig. 3.7 and suppose that the transition between levels 3 and 2 is the signal transition, i.e.

$$E_3 - E_2 = h\nu_S \qquad (3.14)$$

The population of level 2 is not disturbed during pumping and is

$$n_2 = N_2 = N_1 \left[1 - \frac{(E_2 - E_1)}{kT} \right] \qquad (3.15)$$

while the condition for obtaining an inverted population across the signal levels is that n_3 should be greater than n_2. Substitution gives this condition as

$$N_1 - \tfrac{1}{2}N_1 \frac{(E_3 - E_1)}{kT} > N_1 - N_1 \frac{(E_2 - E_1)}{kT}$$

or simply as $\qquad (E_3 - E_1) < 2(E_2 - E_1)$

Thus an inverted population can be maintained across two levels of a three-level system provided that the energy of the pump transition is at least twice that of the signal transition.

The inverted populations are illustrated in Fig. 3.8, and may be compared with the thermal equilibrium populations indi-

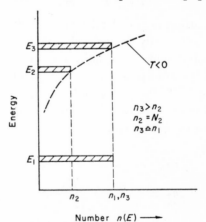

FIG. 3.8   Inverted populations in a three-level system

cated by Fig. 3.9. We may note that whereas the latter shows a normal Maxwell–Boltzmann distribution with a positive value of temperature the corresponding curve for the inverted populations gives a negative value of temperature. This is the 'negative spin temperature'. It is not directly related to the

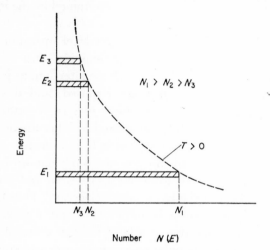

FIG. 3.9   Thermal equilibrium populations in a three-level system

physical temperature of the crystal and is rather to be thought of as an equivalent temperature derived from the population values. Considering levels 3 and 2, the normal population in the upper level in the absence of pumping would be

$$N_3 = N_2 \exp\left[-(E_3 - E_2)/kT\right] \qquad (3.16)$$

which can be rewritten in terms of temperature as

$$T = \frac{-(E_3 - E_2)}{k \log_e\left(\dfrac{N_3}{N_2}\right)} \qquad (3.17)$$

The numerator in equation (3.17) will always be negative because $(E_3 - E_2)$ is positive and in ordinary thermal equili-

37

brium $N_3 < N_2$ so the denominator is negative also and the temperature is positive. After saturation of levels 3 and 1, however, there is an inverted population in which $n_3 > n_2$, so the corresponding term in the denominator is positive giving a negative value of temperature. We may notice that the value of this negative spin temperature is determined by the inversion ratio n_3/n_2.

An important consequence of three-level operation is that the frequency of the valve used for pumping must be at least twice that of the signal. As we shall see later, pump powers of up to a few watts are sometimes required, and this creates difficulties in some shorter wavelength masers. A certain power level is required to saturate the pump levels because in a para-magnetic crystal the spins can couple to the phonon spectrum of the crystal lattice, and this provides a mechanism by which energy can be extracted from the spin system and ultimately dissipated as heat in the lattice and refrigerant. Thus the spins have a certain lifetime in an upper state and a characteristic spin-lattice relaxation time can be defined in terms of the rate at which an inverted population returns to thermal equilibrium due to interaction with the lattice. An inverted population will only be maintained if spins can be raised to the upper level (by absorption at the pump frequency) at a faster rate than the natural decay due to spin-lattice relaxation. Because of this effect the equations given previously for the populations of levels should be modified to take account of spin-lattice relaxa-tion. This leads to the rate equations giving the rate of change of the population of each level; these have been discussed for a number of cases (Bloembergen, 3.2). The results are important for quantitative calculations but do not greatly modify the physical picture of three-level operation presented.

We can now see in outline what the essential features of a simple reflection cavity maser amplifier will be. These are shown in a schematic form in Fig. 3.10. Firstly, a maser crystal is necessary in which there are suitable transitions for the pump and signal frequencies at the same value of magnetic field. Secondly, the crystal must be placed in a microwave cavity which is simultaneously resonant at both the pump and the signal frequencies. The cavity and specimen assembly must also be maintained at low temperatures in a uniform magnetic field

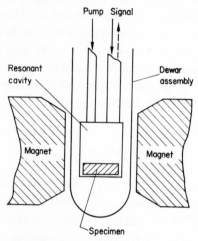

FIG. 3.10 Essential features of a reflection cavity maser

of the correct magnitude. Finally, microwave circuits are needed for a variety of purposes, including separation of the input and amplified output signals and monitoring the pump and signal frequencies. Reference to some of the microwave systems is made in more detail in later Chapters, but some familiarity with methods for the production of uniform magnetic fields (e.g. 3.10) and with low temperature techniques (e.g. 3.11), is assumed.

3.4 Relaxation phenomena

(a) Spin–spin interaction

In the discussions so far the widths of the spectral lines obtained from transitions between the spin levels of a paramagnetic single crystal have not been considered in detail. Knowledge of the linewidth is, however, very important in connection with both maser design and performance, because the bandwidth of a maser can never exceed the linewidth of the signal transition in the paramagnetic single crystal used. Two relaxation mechanisms play a large part in determining the linewidths of the transitions obtained in maser materials. These are the spin-lattice relaxation time T_1, which has already been introduced, and the spin–spin relaxation time T_2. We will be considering spin-lattice relaxation in more detail later and for the moment need only remark that if the spin-lattice relaxation time is T_1 the component of line broadening due to this, ΔB_l, will be approximately

$$\Delta B_l \simeq \frac{1}{T_1} \qquad (3.18)$$

Thus a material having a very short spin-lattice relaxation time will give a very broad line, whereas a material with a large value of T_1 will show negligible line broadening due to this cause. As we have seen from our discussion of pumping, a material with a fairly long spin-lattice relaxation time — usually of the order of several milliseconds or tens of milli-seconds — is used in order to be able to maintain adequate inversion ratios with reasonable pump power levels. Under these conditions the broadening of the line is very small.

The major contribution to the linewidth then comes from spin–spin interaction. At the site of any particular para-magnetic ion variations in the value of the magnetic field may occur because of the influence of the magnetic moments of neighbouring ions to which the particular ion is magnetically coupled. This interaction causes a variation in the local mag-netic field H_l at the site. The value of H_l is given approximately by

$$H_l \simeq \frac{\mu_B}{r^3} \qquad (3.19)$$

where μ_B is the Bohr magneton and r is the distance between neighbouring ions. In many crystals the interatomic spacing is of the order of a few angstrom units, and if the paramagnetic centres are spaced as closely as this local fields of as much as about 1000 oersteds may be obtained. The line broadening ΔB_S due to the spin–spin interaction is related to H_l by the gyromagnetic ratio γ and is

$$\Delta B_S = \gamma H_l \qquad (3.20)$$

(Linewidths can be expressed in terms of either magnetic field or frequency. In experimental measurements oersteds form the natural units. The values may be simply converted to cycles per second because for Zeeman splitting of two levels $h\nu = g\mu_B H$, and for a free spin $\nu/H = 2\cdot8$ Mc/s per oersted.) To reduce the linewidth to values suitable for maser operation — i.e. about 20 oersteds — the spacing between paramagnetic centres must be increased in order to decrease the local field. This is achieved by *magnetic dilution*, i.e. either by growing a mixed crystal diluting the paramagnetic salt with an isomorphous diamagnetic salt (e.g. 0·05% gadolinium ethyl sulphate in 99·95% lanthanum ethyl sulphate) or by substituting a small percentage of a paramagnetic ion for the metallic ion in a diamagnetic host lattice (e.g. 0·05% chromium for aluminium in alumina). In maser materials, which are discussed in detail in Chapter 12, it is usually found that to give suitable linewidths the concentration of the paramagnetic ion should be between about 0·01% and 0·1%.

The spin–spin relaxation time T_2 is defined in terms of the linewidth of the resonance line as

$$T_2 = \frac{1}{B} \qquad (3.21)$$

where B represents the half height linewidth in cycles per second after correction for any other broadening mechanisms (Pryce and Stevens, 3.12). Of the latter that due to hyperfine structure caused by nuclear spin is often one of the most important. In hydrated salts the minimum linewidth is about 6 oersteds because of the nuclear spin of hydrogen and in the cyanides, which crystallize without water of crystallization, the minimum linewidth is reduced to about 1 oersted in very dilute crystals (Bleaney and Stevens, 3.7). The spin–spin relaxation time is a measure of the time taken for energy to be distributed among the individual members of the spin system. This is a fast process and T_2 is usually of the order of 10^{-8} second to 10^{-9} second for most maser crystals.

When considering the observed widths of resonance lines it is useful to distinguish between two classes of broadening which affect the way in which energy is coupled throughout the spin system. We speak of a line being homogeneously broadened if microwave energy absorbed in a resonance experiment is distributed throughout all the spins in the system. This situation will occur in a perfect single crystal observed in a uniform magnetic field and all the spin interactions occur in a time which is very short compared with the spin-lattice relaxation time T_1. If on the other hand the system consists of either an imperfect crystal in a uniform magnetic field or a perfect crystal in an inhomogeneous field the resonance line observed may be inhomogeneously broadened — the spins may be thought of as divided into spin packets each of which contains spins corresponding to a narrow range of magnetic field. The linewidth of the individual spin packets is very much smaller than that of the envelope observed experimentally and the spin packets behave independently. It is thus possible, for example, to saturate some of the spin packets while leaving others undisturbed, a phenomenon known colloquially as *burning a hole in the line*. Inhomogeneous broadening affords a means of artificially increasing the bandwidth of a maser amplifier by introducing a known amount of inhomogeneity into the magnetic field, a technique to which reference is made again in Chapter 6.

(b) Spin-lattice interaction

We have seen that a spin in an upper energy state has a characteristic time, the spin-lattice relaxation time T_1, associated with it and that this measures the rate at which energy is transferred from the spin system to the lattice by coupling with the phonon spectrum of the lattice. The values of the spin-lattice relaxation times for different materials vary over a wide range. For any particular crystal T_1 is temperature dependent and may, over certain concentration ranges, vary in a complex manner with concentration. Knowledge of the spin-lattice relaxation behaviour of paramagnetic crystals is required in order to decide which will be suitable for use in masers and how to establish the optimum operating conditions. Spin-lattice interaction effects also have an important influence on the kind of experimental arrangement necessary for making the basic microwave spectroscopic studies which form a desirable precursor to designing a maser. This arises in the following way.

Suppose the state of magnetization of the paramagnetic crystal in thermal equilibrium is $I(\mathrm{o})$ and that we produce a change in the population distribution, for example by pumping, so that at a subsequent time t the magnetization is $I(t)$. If the pumping signal is removed the system will return to thermal equilibrium and the recovery is governed by the relation

$$\frac{dI(t)}{dt} = -\frac{I(t) - I(\mathrm{o})}{T_1} \tag{3.22}$$

which also defines the spin-lattice relaxation time T_1. Experimental results show that materials in which T_1 is of the order of a few milliseconds are useful and microwave frequencies are of course used to obtain the transitions between levels. Thus in observing resonance lines the r.f. radiation has a period very much less than the spin-lattice relaxation time. In classical terms, regarding the spins as magnetic dipoles, the dipole orientation cannot follow the rapidly changing r.f. magnetic field and in these circumstances it is necessary to use a complex susceptibility. This is written

$$\chi = \chi' - j\chi'' \qquad (3.23)$$

where χ', the real part of the susceptibility, represents the in-phase component and χ'', the imaginary part of the suscepti-

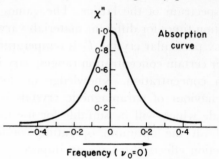

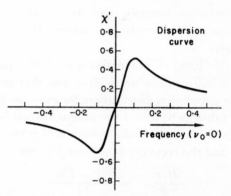

FIG. 3.11 Normalized curves showing the variation with frequency of the real and imaginary parts of the complex susceptibility (ν_0 is the normalized frequency at the centre of the resonance line)

bility, corresponds to the out-of-phase component. Both χ' and χ'' are functions of frequency. Their values have been calculated (e.g. Bloembergen, Purcell and Pound, 3.13) and when the results are plotted graphically curves of the form shown in Fig. 3.11 are obtained. The variation of χ'' gives the absorption

44

curve (whose maximum occurs at resonance when $\nu = \nu_0$) and the variation of χ' corresponds to the dispersion curve.

In studying the microwave spectra of maser crystals we are observing the absorption of radiation and so must have an equipment which can separate χ'' and χ' and select χ'' for examination. One way in which this can be done is by the use

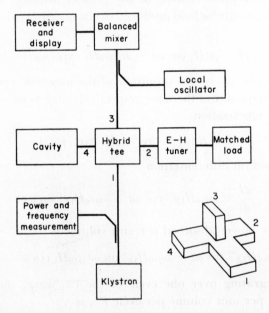

FIG. 3.12 Component layout of a microwave spectrometer showing the use of a hybrid tee junction for separating χ' and χ''

of a magic tee junction and microwave bridge balancing circuit, Fig. 3.12, with which amplitude and phase can be separately adjusted. After initially balancing out the reflected signal from the cavity a small amount of amplitude unbalance is introduced to give the absorption signal. Under these conditions the power absorbed is proportional to χ'' as can be seen as follows. The work W done per unit volume to increase the magnetization I of the crystal in a uniform magnetic field H is the product of

45

the magnetization and the field and so the power absorbed per unit volume P_A is

$$P_A = \frac{dW}{dt} = \mu_0 H \frac{dI}{dt} \tag{3.24}$$

Now the magnetization is itself equal to the product of the field and the susceptibility and, in the present instance, H is the alternating magnetic field produced by the microwave radiation. Thus

$$H = \mu_0 H_1 \cos \omega t = Rl[\mu_0 H_1 \exp (j\omega t)] \tag{3.25}$$

where H_1 and ω are the amplitude of the magnetic vector and angular frequency of the wave respectively and so we can write for the magnetization

$$I = Rl[(\chi' - j\chi'')\mu_0 H_1 \exp (j\omega t)] \tag{3.26}$$

which gives on differentiation

$$\frac{dI}{dt} = \omega \mu_0 H_1 \chi'' \cos \omega t - \omega \mu_0 H_1 \chi' \sin \omega t \tag{3.27}$$

Hence the power absorbed per unit volume is

$$P_A = (\omega \mu_0 H_1 \chi'' \cos \omega t - \omega \mu_0 H_1 \chi' \sin \omega t)\mu_0 H_1 \cos \omega t \tag{3.28}$$

and, integrating over one cycle of the r.f. wave, the power absorbed per unit volume per cycle P'_A is

$$P'_A = \tfrac{1}{2}\omega \mu_0 \chi'' H_1^2 \tag{3.29}$$

From this we can see the importance of the microwave resonant cavity, since the power absorbed is proportional to the square of the field strength of the microwave signal.

The basic process involved in spin-lattice relaxation is the transfer of energy from the spin system to the phonon spectrum of the lattice. The early theories were developed by Kronig (3.14) and Van Vleck (3.15). In these two mechanisms were postulated depending on the temperature of the crystal. At low temperatures each spin couples directly to a lattice phonon of the same energy — the direct process. In this case the spin-lattice relaxation time is given by

$$T_1 = \frac{10^4 \Delta^4}{\lambda^2 H^4 T} \qquad (3.30)$$

in which Δ is the separation (in cm^{-1}) between the two lowest orbital energy levels, λ is the spin-orbit coupling parameter and as usual T is the absolute temperature. Thus at low temperatures, usually below about 8°K, T_1 is inversely proportional to the temperature of the crystal. At higher temperatures more phonon modes can participate and in this region (known as the Raman region) energy can be coupled from a spin to a pair of phonons whose energy difference equals that of the spin. Since there are many pairs of phonons in the phonon spectrum which can satisfy such a condition, the relaxation is much faster and is strongly temperature dependent. The Kronig–Van Vleck model predicts that when this indirect process operates

$$T_1 = \frac{10^4 \Delta^6}{\lambda^2 H^2 T^7} \qquad (3.31)$$

in which we should note the very fast decrease in relaxation time for increasing temperature. This type of behaviour is followed, at least approximately, by many maser crystals and the transition from the T^{-1} to the T^{-7} dependence usually occurs between about 4°K and 20°K. For this reason helium temperatures are normally required for maser operation.

Fig. 3.13 reproduces some spin-lattice relaxation data for 0·05% Cr ruby. Equation (3.30) also suggests in the low temperature range a decrease of T_1 with increasing magnetic field as H^4. Fortunately from the maser viewpoint several materials, notably ruby, do not show such a fast variation, an experimental fact which makes millimetric masers feasible. More recent theories (e.g. Finn, Orbach and Wolf, 3.16) suggest explanations for some of these effects.

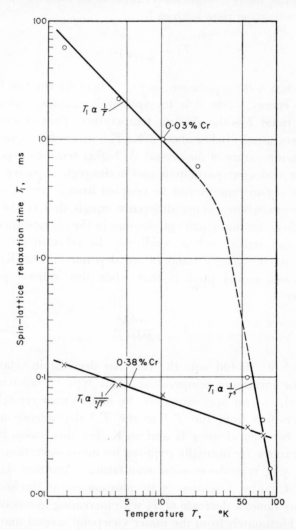

FIG. 3.13 Variation of spin-lattice relaxation time with
temperature in ruby; $\theta = 90°$, 34·6 Gc/s, $+\frac{3}{2}$ to $+\frac{1}{2}$ transition

Table 3.2 gives a selection of experimental values of spin-lattice relaxation time in various maser crystals. From these we can see that to obtain millisecond relaxation times operation at liquid helium temperatures is generally necessary. At 77°K,

Table 3.2

Maser material	Spin-lattice relaxation time ($\Delta s = 1$ transitions)
Potassium chromi-cobalti cyanide (0·05% Cr)	200 ms at 1·25°K, 2·8 kMc/s
	18 ms at 2·16°K, 9·3 kMc/s
	1·3 ms at 1·4°K and 0·6 ms at 4°K, 35 kMc/s
Ruby (0·03–0·05% Cr)	60 ms at 1·4°K, 20 ms at 4°K, 35 kMc/s
	(very similar results at 9 kMc/s)
Sapphire (0·03% Fe)	4 ms at 1·4°K, 1·5 ms at 4°K, 35 kMc/s
Cr rutile (0·07% Cr)	5 ms at 1·4°K, 2·5 ms at 4°K, 35 kMc/s
Fe rutile (∼0·02% Fe)	1 ms at 4°K, 9 kMc/s
Cr doped spinel (0·02% Cr)	20 ms at 1·7°K, 11 ms at 4°K, 9 kMc/s

Selected spin-lattice relaxation time (T_1) data for some maser materials

liquid nitrogen temperature, most materials have relaxation times in the microsecond range and with these short values it is not possible (with a few exceptions we shall mention later) to maintain a sufficient inversion ratio for maser operation to be obtained.

(c) Measurement of spin-lattice relaxation times
Several techniques have been used to measure relaxation times. Of these one of the most widely used is the pulse saturation method. The apparatus required for this is indicated by Fig. 3.14 from which we see that a microwave spectrometer is modified by adding a facility for introducing a high power

microwave pulse into the resonant cavity. In studying the resonance transition between two given energy levels the absorption line is normally observed with a low incident power level ($\sim$ microwatts) so that a negligible change is produced in the population distribution. The d.c. magnetic field is adjusted

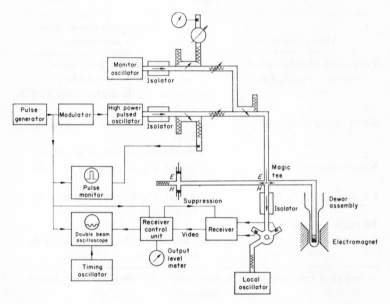

FIG. 3.14   Component arrangement for measurement of spin-lattice relaxation times by the pulse saturation method

for resonance and display instrumentation arranged to record the absorption in the crystal. If a high power pulse of the same frequency is applied the levels will be saturated and hence, instantaneously, no absorption can occur since the populations of the two levels are equal. Once the high power pulse ceases spin-lattice relaxation occurs and the absorption will recover exponentially to the value corresponding to thermal equilibrium, Fig. 3.15. When the recovery can be represented by a single exponential the recovery rate is taken as the spin-lattice relaxation time.

Although approximately single exponential relaxation is observed in many crystals the levels are in fact coupled so that a perturbation of any pair of levels affects all the others to some extent by cross-relaxation (Shapiro and Bloembergen, 3.17). A particularly interesting example of this is in harmonic cross-

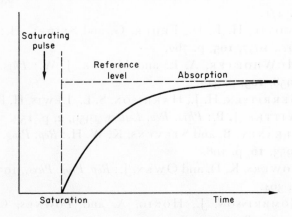

FIG. 3.15 Sequence of operations in the pulse saturation technique

relaxation. In several maser crystals situations can arise at certain polar angles where the levels are either equispaced or are separated by amounts which are harmonically related to each other. Under these conditions it is possible for several microwave phonons to excite a transition across a harmonic level. Equally, spin-lattice relaxation may occur by multi-phonon as well as by single-phonon processes and this results in a severe reduction of the effective T_1. In ordinary three-level maser operation cross-relaxation orientations are avoided for this reason. It has been shown, however, that it is possible to utilize harmonic cross-relaxation to obtain maser amplification at frequencies higher than the pump frequency (e.g. Siegman, 3.18), an achievement not possible with normal three-level operation.

References

3.1   RAMSEY, N. F.: *Quantum Electronics III* (Columbia University Press, 1964), p. 333.

3.2   BLOEMBERGEN, N.: *Phys. Rev.*, 1956, **104**, p. 324.

3.3   SCHULTZ–DU BOIS, E. O.: *Bell Syst. Tech. J.*, 1959, **38**, p. 271.

3.4   SCOVIL, H. E. D., FEHER, G. and SEIDEL, H.: *Phys. Rev.*, 1957, **105**, p. 762.

3.5   McWHORTER, A. L. and MEYER, J. W.: *Phys. Rev.*, 1958, **109**, p. 312.

3.6   GERRITSEN, H. J., HARRISON, S. E., LEWIS, H. R. and WITTKE, J. P.: *Phys. Rev. Letters*, 1959, **2**, p. 153.

3.7   BLEANEY, B. and STEVENS, K. W. H.: *Rep. Prog. Phys.*, 1953, **16**, p. 108.

3.8   BOWERS, K. D. and OWEN, J.: *Rep. Prog. Phys.*, 1955, **18**, p. 304.

3.9   COMBRISSON, J., HONIG, A. and TOWNES, C. H.: *Comptes Rendus*, 1956, **242**, p. 245.

3.10 DE KLERK, D.: *The Construction of High Field Electromagnets* (Newport Instruments Ltd., 1965).

3.11 WHITE, G. K.: *Experimental Technique in Low Temperature Physics* (Oxford University Press, 1959).

3.12 PRYCE, M. H. L. and STEVENS, K. W. H.: *Proc. Phys. Soc. A*, 1950, **63**, p. 36.

3.13 BLOEMBERGEN, N., PURCELL, E. M. and POUND, R. V.: *Phys. Rev.*, 1948, **73**, p. 679.

3.14 KRONIG, R. DE L.: *Physica*, 1939, **6**, p. 33.

3.15 VAN VLECK, J. H.: *Phys. Rev.*, 1948, **74**, p. 1168.

3.16 FINN, C. B. P., ORBACH R. and WOLF, W. P.: *Proc. Phys Soc.*, 1961, **77**, p. 261.

3.17 SHAPIRO, S. and BLOEMBERGEN, N.: *Phys. Rev.*, 1959, **116**, p. 1453.

3.18 SIEGMAN, A. E.: *Microwave Solid State Masers* (McGraw-Hill, 1964), p. 503.

4

C.W. Solid State Masers

W E have seen in preceding Chapters what the physical requirements are for maser operation. For convenience they will be summarized again briefly. A suitable crystal must be placed in a microwave structure which is resonant simultaneously at both the signal and pump frequencies. This assembly must in turn be placed in a low temperature environment and an external d.c. magnetic field must in general be applied to obtain the Zeeman splitting appropriate to the frequencies used. This Chapter shows how these conditions may be achieved in practice and indicates what kind of performance may be obtained by describing four types of maser which can amplify continuously (the term c.w., standing for continuous wave, maser is often used to describe this situation). The steps involved in calculating maser gain, bandwidth and noise performance are also outlined.

4.1 Three-level cavity masers

(a) Design features
One of the first solid state masers to operate successfully was that of Scovil, Feher and Seidel (4.1). This used gadolinium/ cerium ethyl sulphate as the maser material (0·5% gadolinium

ethyl sulphate grown as a single crystal with 99·2% lanthanum ethyl sulphate as an isomorphous diamagnetic dilutant with 0·2% cerium added, Gd/La $(C_2H_5SO_4)_3.9H_2O)$. The active paramagnetic ion was Gd^{3+} and by double doping with cerium the relaxation times of the signal and pump transitions were made to differ by a factor of ten enabling a relatively low pump power to be used. The energy level scheme is shown in

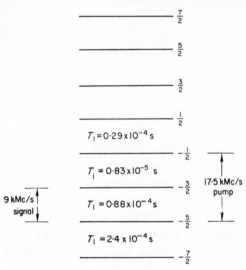

Fig. 4.1   Energy level system for gadolinium ethyl sulphate
(the relaxation times refer to 4°K)

Fig. 4.1, and by pumping at 17·5 kMc/s across the $-\frac{5}{2}$ to $-\frac{1}{2}$ transition amplification at 9 kMc/s was obtained across the $-\frac{5}{2}$ to $-\frac{3}{2}$ transition at $\theta = 90°$. We should take special notice of the cavity used, Fig. 4.2, because it illustrates one way in which the requirement for simultaneous resonance at both the pump and signal frequencies may be met. The K-band pump power was fed down a strip transmission line to a resonant plate mounted in an X-band cavity terminating the X-band signal waveguide (there is no general rule for cavity design and a variety of different techniques have been used in

54

different masers). In order to obtain finite transition probabilities for the pump and signal transitions the d.c. magnetic field of 2850 oersteds was applied at 45° to the respective r.f. magnetic fields which were parallel with this cavity. The maser operated successfully at liquid helium temperatures. As a maser material, however, gadolinium ethyl sulphate has several drawbacks (referred to in Chapter 12) and its use has not been pursued.

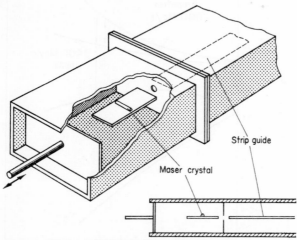

FIG. 4.2   The Scovil, Feher and Seidel maser cavity for 9000 Mc/s operation

An example of a reflection cavity maser is the 2800 Mc/s amplifier described by McWhorter and Meyer (4.2). They used potassium chromicobalticyanide, $K_3(Cr \cdot Co)(CN)_6$, as the maser material; this is a crystal which can fairly readily be grown from aqueous solution and has a convenient splitting D of 0·083 cm^{-1} with spin-lattice relaxation times of up to 500 ms at chromium concentrations of about 0·05%. The Cr^{3+} ion gives four energy levels in a magnetic field and these are shown for $\theta = 0°$ in Fig. 4.3. The crystal was mounted at the base of the cylindrical cavity shown in Fig. 4.4, from which we can see that the 9000 Mc/s (X-band) pump power was coupled by an

55

iris from the waveguide feed to the cavity, whereas the 2800 Mc/s (S-band) signal was introduced by a loop at the end of a coaxial cable. The cylinder and post construction enabled resonant modes to be supported at both frequencies. This assembly was placed in a low temperature cryostat between the

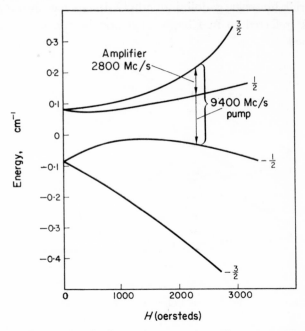

FIG. 4.3   Energy level scheme for potassium chromicyanide showing signal and pump transitions for 2800 Mc/s operation ($\theta = 0°$)

poles of an electromagnet giving a field of about 2400 oersteds directed along the crystalline c-axis. In a maser there is a good deal of associated microwave electronics and control instrumentation. Some idea of this is given in the diagrammatic layout of Fig. 4.5. Without giving details of this aspect of masers it is worth repeating that usually frequency stabilization of the klystrons is necessary, that the magnetic field must be stable and homogeneous to about 1 part in 10^5 over the specimen volume, and that particular care is necessary in the microwave bridge circuits. The maser operated in the liquid helium temperature range giving gains of up to about 20 dB with bandwidths of a few hundred kilocycles.

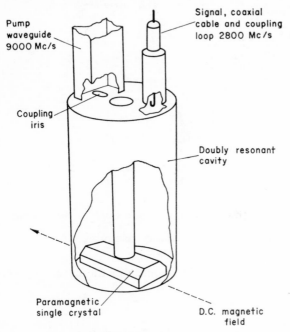

FIG. 4.4   The McWhorter and Meyer cavity for 2800 Mc/s operation

More recently ruby, Cr^{3+} in Al_2O_3, has become very popular as a material for centimetric masers. The reasons for this are considered in Chapter 12, but from the point of view of cavity design two important factors arise. The first of these is that the dielectric constant is relatively high ($\epsilon \sim 12$), and the second that quite large single crystals can be obtained. This enables the specimen itself to be used as a dielectric resonant cavity and so allows a very high filling factor to be obtained. Fig. 4.6 shows one example of this, a ruby maser cavity for X-band operation with K-band pumping designed by Morris, Kyhl and Strandberg

E

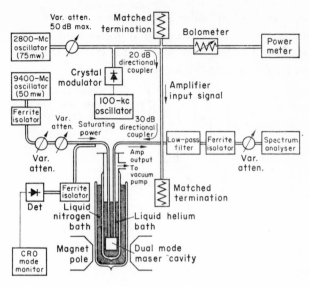

FIG. 4.5   General layout of a cavity maser assembly

(4.3). Many other ruby maser assemblies have used similar arrangements with waveguide inputs for both the pump and signal frequencies which resonate in the cavity in orthogonal modes.

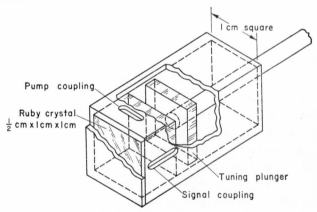

FIG. 4.6   The Morris, Kyhl and Strandberg ruby maser cavity
(*X*-band signal, *K*-band pumping)

(b) Gain and bandwidth

In calculating the gain of a cavity maser we can regard it simply as a circuit element and utilize equivalent circuit ideas in a straightforward manner. With masers as with other conventional types of amplifier the gain and bandwidth are intimately connected. Thus it is possible to have a high gain with a narrow bandwidth or vice versa, but not high gain and high bandwidth together.

Regarding the question of gain (4.4, 4.5) a useful approach is to think of the voltage standing wave ratio r and reflection coefficients Γ of the reflection maser cavity. A result from circuit theory is that

$$\Gamma = \frac{r-1}{r+1} \qquad (4.1)$$

and if a power P_i is incident on the cavity the reflected power P_r is given simply by

$$\frac{P_r}{P_i} = \Gamma^2 = \frac{(r-1)^2}{(r+1)^2} \qquad (4.2)$$

It is convenient to express the results in terms of cavity Q factors since these may be measured experimentally. A maser cavity assembly consists of a resonant cavity which is usually coupled by an iris to an external waveguide system giving the two corresponding Q values Q_0 (the unloaded cavity Q) and Q_e respectively. As we have seen in Chapter 3 the paramagnetic crystal also has a Q value because as it is in an oscillating magnetic field it stores magnetic energy and Q_m, the magnetic Q of the crystal, is defined as

$$Q_m = \frac{1}{4\pi\chi''\eta} \qquad (4.3)$$

where χ'' is the imaginary part of the susceptibility and η is the filling factor. The filling factor is usually taken as the ratio of the crystal volume to the cavity volume and in different cavity designs may vary in magnitude from about $0 \cdot 1$ to $1 \cdot 0$.

The loaded Q of the cavity Q_L is given from the equivalent circuit as

$$\frac{1}{Q_L} = \frac{1}{Q_e} + \frac{1}{Q_m} + \frac{1}{Q_0} \qquad (4.4)$$

and the standing wave ratio looking into a cavity whose resonant frequency is $\omega_0/2\pi$ is given by

$$r = \frac{\dfrac{1}{Q_e}}{\dfrac{1}{Q_L} - \dfrac{1}{Q_e} + j\left(\dfrac{\omega}{\omega_0} - \dfrac{\omega_0}{\omega}\right)} \qquad (4.5)$$

where $\omega/2\pi$ is the frequency of the incident radiation (4.6). At resonance $\omega = \omega_0$ so equation (4.5) reduces to

$$r = \frac{1}{\left(\dfrac{Q_e}{Q_L} - 1\right)} \qquad (4.6)$$

and using equations (4.1) and (4.2) to relate the standing wave ratio to the ratio of reflected to incident power it can be found that

$$\frac{P_r}{P_i} = \frac{\left(\dfrac{Q_e}{Q_0} + \dfrac{Q_e}{Q_m} - 1\right)^2}{\left(\dfrac{Q_e}{Q_0} + \dfrac{Q_e}{Q_m} + 1\right)^2} \qquad (4.7)$$

In an amplifier it is more useful to obtain an explicit relation for the gain G. Dividing both the numerator and denominator of the right-hand side of equation (4.7) by Q_e^2 gives

$$G = \frac{P_r}{P_i} = \frac{\left(\dfrac{1}{Q_0} + \dfrac{1}{Q_m} - \dfrac{1}{Q_e}\right)}{\left(\dfrac{1}{Q_0} + \dfrac{1}{Q_m} + \dfrac{1}{Q_e}\right)} \qquad (4.8)$$

Some simplifications can now be made because, as we have seen, a maser normally operates at high gain. This means that

Q_0 will be large compared with the other Q values and so terms in $1/Q_0$ can be neglected. This gives

$$G = \frac{Q_e - Q_m}{Q_e + Q_m} \qquad (4.9)$$

Since Q_m is always negative for stimulated emission an alternative form of this is

$$G = \frac{Q_e + |Q_m|}{Q_e - |Q_m|} \qquad (4.10)$$

In the cavity maser the width of the paramagnetic resonance line is usually very much greater than that of the cavity which must have a high Q_0 and hence a narrow bandwidth to achieve the required amount of gain. The maser bandwidth B is then determined by the cavity and is given simply by

$$B = \frac{Q_L}{f_0} \qquad (4.11)$$

where f_0 is the cavity resonant frequency. Expressing Q_L in terms of Q_e and Q_m and assuming again that $1/Q_0$ is very small

$$B = f_0 \frac{(Q_m - Q_e)}{Q_m Q_e} \qquad (4.12)$$

Since, as we have seen, the gain and bandwidth are interrelated it is usual to give the gain bandwidth product rather than the separate values of B and G. However, since the maser is used as a voltage amplifier, it is appropriate to use the square root of the power gain given by equation (4.10) when making the multiplication. This leads to the expression for the root gain–bandwidth product

$$G^{\frac{1}{2}}B = f_0 \frac{(Q_e + |Q_m|)}{Q_e |Q_m|} \qquad (4.13)$$

From this we see that to optimize the root gain–bandwidth product the external Q should be nearly equal to the magnetic Q, i.e. $Q_e \simeq Q_m$. (This may be achieved in practice by providing a fine control on the cavity coupling.) Under these conditions

$$G^{\frac{1}{2}}B \simeq \frac{2f_0}{|Q_m|} \qquad (4.14)$$

which indicates the advantage of making Q_m small.

In the McWhorter and Meyer maser described above the theoretical value of Q_m was $Q_m = -2150$. The signal frequency was 2800 Mc/s, i.e.

$$f_0 = 2 \cdot 8 \times 10^8 \text{ c/s}$$

and so from equation (4.14) the predicted root gain–band-width product was

$$G^{\frac{1}{2}}B = \frac{2f_0}{|Q_m|} = 2 \cdot 6 \times 10^6 \text{ s}^{-1}$$

The experimental value of $G^{\frac{1}{2}}B$ was found to be $1 \cdot 8 \times 10^6$ s^{-1} which we can regard as very good agreement in view of the approximations made in deriving equation (4.14). In a similar manner most cavity masers give gains of up to about 20 dB with bandwidths of a few hundred kilocycles.

4.2 The push–pull maser

One of the features of the energy level systems of many para-magnetic materials mentioned earlier was that they were dependent on the polar angle θ between the crystallographic axis of the crystal and the d.c. magnetic field. An important example of the use of this feature is the push–pull cavity maser.

In ruby the Cr^{3+} ion, having an effective spin value of 3/2, produces four energy levels in a d.c. magnetic field and, as we have seen above, there is a considerable degree of choice in combining energy level and polar angle considerations to obtain straightforward three-level operation at some particular frequency. On changing θ, however, a position can be found, at $\theta = 54° 44'$, where the four energy levels are split so that the upper levels 3 and 4 are mirror images in energy of the lower levels 2 and 1. This symmetrical situation is shown in Fig. 4.7. At this particular polar angle the transitions between levels 1 and 3 and between levels 2 and 4 become degenerate for all values of the external d.c. magnetic field. A single pump frequency chosen to excite an absorptive transition between

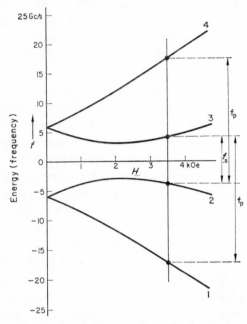

FIG. 4.7   Energy level diagram for ruby in the 'push–pull' orientation at $\theta = 54° 44'$

levels 1 and 3 will therefore also be absorbed simultaneously at the same value of magnetic field by the 2–4 transition. Taking the signal transition between levels 3 and 2, the population of level 3 is increased as in normal three-level operation but at the same time the population of level 2 is reduced. This mode of operation, for which four suitable energy levels are essential, is commonly known as either *push–pull action* or *double pumping*. Because the population of the lower level of the signal transition

63

is depleted a higher inversion ratio can be obtained than in straightforward three-level operation. Calculations show that in ruby at low temperatures push–pull pumping should be about six times more efficient than single pumping.

The fact that a larger population difference can be obtained across the signal levels has a direct bearing on the temperature at which maser action may take place. As we have just seen, conventional three-level cavity masers usually operate at liquid helium temperatures (where the spin-lattice relaxation times are reasonably long), but with push–pull pumping the possibility exists of achieving a sufficient population difference at higher temperatures despite the reductions in relaxation times. This was first demonstrated by Ditchfield and Forrester (4.7), who observed maser action in the region of 60°K in a push–pull ruby cavity maser. In this maser the cavity was a right circular cylinder, split midway along its axis to permit introduction of the nominal 0·1% Cr ruby specimen, which supported the TE_{013} mode at pump frequencies near 24 kMc/s (K-band) and the TE_{111} mode at signal frequencies near 9·3 kMc/s (X-band). The pump power was coupled to the cavity through an iris at the end of a waveguide feed and the signal power by a loop terminating a coaxial cable. The cavity assembly was enclosed in a conventional double Dewar system, the outer holding liquid nitrogen at atmospheric pressure and the inner containing the refrigerant pumped to a low pressure. For experiments between 78°K and about 63°K liquid nitrogen was used as the refrigerant. However, below 63·2°K (where nitrogen at reduced pressure is solid) difficulties were encountered due to insufficient thermal contact between the refrigerant and the cavity assembly. For the lower temperature range from 63°K to about 56°K liquid oxygen, whose triple point is at 54·4°K, was found to be preferable. Amplification was observed at frequencies between 9280 Mc/s and 9520 Mc/s at temperatures near 60°K. The cavity had a Q value of 20 000 and stable gains of up to 30 dB were achieved by over-coupling at the signal frequency. The root gain–bandwidth product was measured and found to be

$$G^{\frac{1}{2}}B = 3 \cdot 8 \text{ Mc/s}$$

where B is the bandwidth to the half power points and G is the gain. This product remained constant for input signal levels between 10^{-12} watts and 10^{-7} watts.

In operating the push–pull maser it was found, as indeed we might expect, that the alignment of the ruby crystal was very critical. The crystal was aligned by observing at room temperature either the occurrence of degeneracy between the pump transitions or of absorption lines at the signal frequency between levels 2 and 1 and between 3 and 4. At 56°K there was no stimulated emission if the crystal was misorientated away from $\theta = 54° 44'$ by more than $1°$. This criticality has been confirmed by later work on x-band push–pull masers and the influence of crystal quality in this respect is discussed in later Chapters.

We can readily appreciate that the chief practical advantage of push–pull operation is that liquid helium is not required. This not only simplifies the maser equipment but makes low noise amplifiers feasible in locations where liquid helium is not readily available. Subsequent development of push–pull masers has been mainly concentrated at x-band (since many of the communications applications are in this wavelength region) and has followed the development of higher power pump sources at k-band. The latter band is not generally used for communications or radar because the wavelengths are near to a strong absorption in water vapour. In particular attention has been given to improving the filling factor by using large ruby samples as dielectric cavities, to increasing the bandwidth and to obtaining operation at liquid nitrogen temperatures. The push–pull maser is now a well-established type of device though, as yet, it appears that a suitable symmetrical energy level scheme is only obtainable in ruby.

4.3 Travelling wave masers

(a) Slow wave structures

We may recall that when comparing various conventional microwave amplifier tubes we find that the narrow bandwidth limitation of valves based on resonant cavities, e.g. klystrons (4.8), can be overcome by using the periodic interaction between electrons and the r.f. field obtainable in the slow wave structure of a travelling wave tube (4.9). In a similar way in the travelling wave maser the use of a slow wave structure instead of a resonant cavity permits a much greater bandwidth than is possible with a cavity maser. The travelling wave maser (often referred to as the TWM) has other advantages over its cavity counterpart and probably represents the best practical embodiment of the maser principle.

A slow wave waveguide structure is one in which the velocity of propagation of electromagnetic radiation is less than that in free space. In such a structure concentration of the r.f. field can be obtained. The power P in a wave travelling in a slow wave structure is related to the energy stored per unit length of the structure W_s by the simple relation

$$P = v_g W_s \qquad (4.15)$$

where v_g is the group velocity of the wave. The value of W_s is given by integrating the square of the r.f. field over the cross-sectional area of the structure. The shape of the structure determines the velocity reduction and if this is large W_s will also be large. This means that, for a given incident power level, the r.f. field can be made large by designing a structure to give a large velocity reduction.

The presence of r.f. field concentration in a slow wave structure corresponds to that obtainable through the Q factor of a resonant cavity. Thus if a maser crystal is placed in a slow wave structure maser operation should be possible. There are several important differences, however. The energy given out

66

by an element of maser material in the TWM leads to an increase in the r.f. field travelling along the structure and so increases the rate of emission of energy from succeeding elements, but it does not react (as in a cavity) with the original element. Thus regeneration and oscillation, which are inherent in the cavity system, can only occur in the TWM as a result of reflections in the external microwave circuit. Because the passbands of the structures employed are very large the bandwidth of the TWM is mainly determined by the paramagnetic resonance linewidth of the maser material and decreases only gradually with increasing gain. Furthermore, the TWM can be designed to be completely non-reciprocal. This greatly simplifies the external waveguide system since there is no need for the ancillary non-reciprocal components essential for cavity maser operation.

(b) Design considerations

In discussing some of the other design considerations of the TWM, in particular the question of the most suitable type of slow wave structure, it is convenient first of all to take some data for ruby and, by substitution in the equations given below, find the values of some of the design parameters. The value of Q_m depends, of course, on the level scheme adopted and the operating temperature but can for 0·05% Cr ruby be quite low. In the maser described by Walling and Smith (4.10), for use in the General Post Office Satellite Communication Ground Station at Goonhilly Down, a 90° orientation was used with a signal frequency of 4170 Mc/s and the value of Q_m was $Q_m \sim 6$ at 1·5°K. The gain of the TWM is shown by equation (4.22) to be proportional to the length of the structure, but in practice the length cannot usefully be increased beyond about 10 cm. The reasons for this are the difficulties in manufacturing longer slow wave structures to the accuracy required, in obtaining large homogeneous single crystals and in producing magnetic fields of high uniformity over a large volume.

67

The gain equation also shows that to obtain a high gain for a given length of structure the group velocity should be as small as possible, indicating the desirability of a structure with a large slowing factor (the ratio between the free space velocity of light and the wave group velocity in the structure v_g). There are in fact two requirements, the first to use a large slowing factor and the second to provide simultaneously regions where the

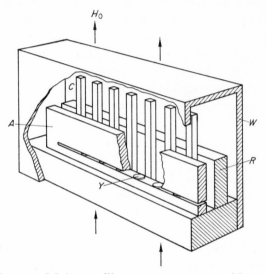

FIG. 4.8   4170 Mc/s travelling wave maser assembly; cut-away view showing comb structure

r.f. magnetic fields are circularly polarized in opposite senses. It has been found that the comb structure best suits these requirements. This was used in the first operational ruby TWM described by De Grasse, Schultz–du Bois and Scovil (4.11) and has subsequently been widely adopted, notably by Walling and Smith. The comb structure consists of an array of conductors, each a quarter of a wavelength long at the signal frequency, mounted centrally in a waveguide and short circuited at one end. The r.f. magnetic field of the propagated wave is in the plane normal to the conductors and is circularly polarized in opposite senses on the two sides of the array. An example of a complete ruby TWM assembly using a comb structure is shown in Fig. 4.8. Here there is a structure C of 2 mm pitch which permits propagation of the 4170 Mc/s signal frequency at a group velocity of rather less than one-hundredth of that of light in free space. The ruby single crystal R is placed on one side of the array. The signal transition used is between levels 1–4 at 4170 Mc/s, obtained at $\theta = 90°$ in a steady magnetic field H of 3280 oersteds. Backward waves are attenuated by yttrium iron garnet discs Y which are held in place by a polycrystalline slab of alumina A. The transmission characteristics of the slow wave structure can be adjusted by the thin Melinex sheet M inserted between the array and the alumina. The pump power, at 30150 Mc/s, is transmitted directly down the waveguide W. The size of the assembly is shown by the dimensioned cross-section shown in Fig. 4.9.

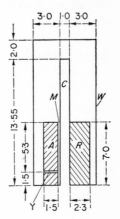

FIG. 4.9 4170 Mc/s travelling wave maser assembly; cross-sectional diagram giving dimensions (mm)

As Chapter 6 refers to some detailed performance data of TWM's in connection with maser applications only one important feature will be pointed out here. The noise temperature of a TWM is, like its cavity counterpart, very low — usually of the order of a few degrees absolute. The calculation of noise temperature follows the same general scheme as that for the cavity system except that allowance must be made for the distributed structure. The temperature T_a of the input lead to the TWM is very important and must be kept low because it can contribute appreciably to the value of overall equivalent noise temperature T_n. The latter is given by

$$T_n = \frac{1}{1-\alpha}\left(\alpha T_a + \frac{T_0}{I}\right) \qquad (4.16)$$

69

where α is the absorption coefficient of the input lead, T_0 is the ambient temperature of the active maser material and I is the population inversion. Typically a TWM operated at 4°K will have an inversion factor of about three. By careful design the input lead losses may be reduced to about o·2 dB and if the mean temperature of the lead can be kept down to about 100°K overall equivalent noise temperatures of about 6°K can be obtained.

✳ (c) *Theory of the TWM*

The small signal gain of a TWM can be expressed in terms of the two quality factors Q_0 and Q_m. The value of Q_0, the intrinsic quality factor for the slow wave structure, is determined by the dielectric and ohmic power loss per unit length of structure P_0. The magnetic quality factor Q_m of the maser material is determined by the power P_m emitted per unit length of material. Thus there are two basic relations as follows:

$$\frac{1}{Q_m} = \frac{P_m}{2\pi f W_s} \qquad (4.17)$$

and

$$\frac{1}{Q_0} = \frac{P_0}{2\pi f W_s} \qquad (4.18)$$

where f is the operating frequency. Consider now the energy emitted by a small element of maser material of length dz situated at some point along the TWM as shown in Fig. 4.10.

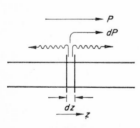

FIG. 4.10 Emission from an element of a travelling wave maser

A property of travelling wave structures is that only forward travelling increments of field add in phase so virtually all the energy emitted travels in the forward direction. Allowing for absorption in the element, however, the change in power level dp across the element dz becomes

$$dp = (P_m - P_0)dz \qquad (4.19)$$

By combining equations (4.17), (4.18) and (4.19) dp can be expressed in terms of Q_m and Q_0. Thus

$$dp = 2\pi f W_s \left(\frac{1}{Q_m} - \frac{1}{Q_0} \right) dz \qquad (4.20)$$

and replacing W_s by $\dfrac{P}{v_g}$ from equation (4.15) gives

$$dp = P 2\pi f \frac{1}{v_g} \left(\frac{1}{Q_m} - \frac{1}{Q_0} \right) dz \qquad (4.21)$$

Integration for a finite length L of maser material gives the expression for the net gain in dB G_n

$$G_n = 20\pi \log_{10} e \frac{fL}{v_g} \left(\frac{1}{Q_m} - \frac{1}{Q_0} \right) \qquad (4.22)$$

or more concisely,

$$G = 27\cdot3 fL \frac{1}{v_g} \left(\frac{1}{Q_m} - \frac{1}{Q_0} \right) \qquad (4.23)$$

From this expression we see that in order to obtain a high gain with a reasonable length of structure the requirements are to keep Q_m small, Q_0 large and v_g as small as possible. The first term in the expression for the net gain is often called the electronic gain G_0, and represents the gain that would be obtained with a perfect lossless structure. The practical result of this theory is that it defines the main problem in designing a TWM, namely that both v_g and Q_m are determined by the way in which the propagating slow wave structure and the active maser material are combined.

The group velocity v_g is determined by the r.f. properties of the structure and special slow wave comb structures have been developed in which waves are propagated with group velocities of about one-hundredth of the free space velocity of light. The parameter Q_m, of course, depends on the paramagnetic properties of the active maser material, and Walling and Smith have shown that its value for a TWM is given by

$$\frac{1}{Q_m} = \Delta n h\gamma^2 \frac{\phi(f)\eta}{2(1+R)} \left[(A+B)^2 + R(A-B)^2 \right.$$
$$\left. + 2\cos 2\theta_1(A^2 - B^2)R^{\frac{1}{2}}\right] \quad (4.24)$$

In this expression A and B are the matrix element vectors at the signal transition frequency (whose values are listed by Siegman, 3.18) and Δn is the inverted population difference between the signal levels. The parameter $\phi(f)$ is a line shape function and when dipole–dipole or spin–spin interaction is the dominant process governing the lineshape has a Lorentzian form. Thus

$$\phi(f) = \frac{2T_2}{4\pi^2(f-f_0)^2 + 1/T_2} \quad (4.25)$$

where T_2 is the spin–spin relaxation time and f_0 the resonant frequency. As usual η, the filling factor, represents the fraction of the total magnetic energy stored in the maser material. The angle θ_1 is that between the larger matrix element vector and the major axis of the elliptically polarized r.f. magnetic field. The degree of ellipticity of the field is denoted by R, defined so that for linear polarization $R = 1$ and for circular polarization $R = 0$ or $R = \infty$ depending on the sense of the polarization. Combining the equations given above gives an expression for the bandwidth of the TWM. Assuming the use of a material giving Lorentzian lineshapes so that equation (4.25) holds for $\phi(f)$ the bandwidth B to half power points is

$$B = \frac{1}{\pi T_2} \sqrt{\left(\frac{3}{G_0 - 3}\right)} \quad (4.26)$$

where as before G_0 is the electronic gain in a uniform d.c. magnetic field. This relation is plotted in Fig. 4.11 taking the value of $T_2 = 4.9 \times 10^{-9}$ s for the spin–spin relaxation time in ruby. We can see that the useful gains can be obtained with bandwidths far in excess of those possible with cavity systems.

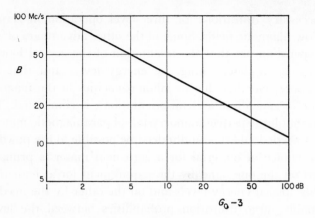

FIG. 4.11 Bandwidth–gain characteristic of a TWM. Uniform magnetic field operation, spin–spin relaxation time taken as 4.9×10^{-9} s

✳ 4.4 Zero field masers

As we have seen a basic requirement of three level masers, such as those described so far in this Chapter, is that non-zero magnetic dipole transition probabilities should exist between the participating levels. We have also seen that, since the selection rule $M = 1$ applies, this cannot be fulfilled when the quantization of angular momentum is of pure spin. This difficulty can be overcome by using the Zeeman levels of a paramagnetic salt having Stark splitting, in which case the quantization is very mixed and transitions may generally take place between all levels. It is of course for this reason that a magnetic field is required in masers of this type. From the user's point of view, however, the necessity for a highly homogeneous magnetic field is a disadvantage because magnets and their associated stabilized power supplies tend to be bulky and expensive. The possibility of achieving maser action without a magnetic field has been investigated by several workers, in particular Bogle and Symmons (4.12), and it turns out that there are several paramagnetic substances which can provide

F

the necessary transitions for three-level operation in zero or very low magnetic fields. Some of the other advantages of zero field operation are that the orientation of the crystal loses its importance in determining the energy levels and that line broadening, whether due to inhomogeneities in the magnetic field or to crystalline axis misorientations, is eliminated. This means that large perfect monocrystals of paramagnetic material are not needed and it would indeed be possible to use powders.

The choice of material for a zero field maser is primarily limited on the one hand by the requirement for at least three suitably spaced energy levels and on the other by the need for reasonably large transition probabilities between the levels. The first question is the choice of spin value, i.e. of which paramagnetic ion to use. We know that the number of independent states of an ion with spin S is $(2S + 1)$. However, the number of distinct energy levels cannot, by Kramers theorem, exceed $(S + \frac{1}{2})$ for integral-plus-a-half spin values. Of course the full $(2S + 1)$ levels are obtainable for integral spin values. Therefore, if the lattice has sufficiently low symmetry to allow the full multiplicity to be obtained, there are available, from the possibilities shown in Table 4.1, only those

Table 4.1

Spin	$\frac{1}{2}$	I	$\frac{3}{2}$	2	$\frac{5}{2}$	$\frac{7}{2}$
Number of levels	I	3	2	5	3	4
Ion	Cu^{2+}	Ni^{2+}	Cr^{3+}	Cr^{2+}	Fe^{3+}	Gd^{3+}

Spin values of various paramagnetic ions and the number of levels obtained in zero field operation

spin values giving three or more levels, i.e. all ions having spin values other than $\frac{1}{2}$ or $\frac{3}{2}$.

The second question concerns transition probabilities. These are most readily indicated by reference to the spin Hamiltonian. The most commonly occurring form of Hamiltonian in zero magnetic field is

$$\mathscr{H} = D[S_z^2 - \tfrac{1}{3}S(S + 1)] \tag{4.27}$$

where z represents a symmetry axis of the internal crystalline electric field. However, a material with a Hamiltonian of this form will not be suitable for a zero field maser because here the eigenstates of energy are also eigenstates of S_z since $\mathscr{H}$ and S_z commute. The eigenvalues of equation (4.27) are given by

$$E_M = D[M^2 - \tfrac{1}{3}S(S + 1)] \qquad (4.28)$$

where M is the eigenvalue of S_z. We obtain a series of levels in the order $M = 0, \pm 1, \pm 2$, etc. for integral spins and $M = \pm\frac{1}{2}$, $\pm\frac{3}{2}$, etc. for half integral spins. This is forbidden when normal selection rules apply. In quite a number of paramagnetic salts, however, the internal crystalline field has lower symmetry elements present and the term S_z^2 in equation (4.27) is accompanied by others representing, for example, rhombic, trigonal, tetragonal or hexagonal symmetry components. The resulting Hamiltonians are such that the lower symmetry terms do not commute with S_z so the eigenstates of $\mathscr{H}$ are not pure eigenstates of S_z and the normal selection rules no longer apply.

Some of the zero field maser properties of Cr^{2+} and Ni^{2+} ions are given in Table 4.2. Here the transition probabilities

Table 4.2

Salt	Temperature of measurement (°K)	Pumping frequency (Mc/s)	Pumping probability for powdered salt (free-spin units)	Amplifying frequency (Mc/s)	Amplifying probability for powdered salt (free-spin units)	Difference frequency (Mc/s)
$CrSO_4.5H_2O$	290	(a) 77 000	4	18 000	1·3	59 000
		(b) 270 000	0·01	77 000	4	190 000
		(c) 270 000	0·01	59 000	4	210 000
$K_2Ni(SO_4)_2.6H_2O$	290	115 000	1·7	30 000	1·7	85 000
$(NH_4)_2Ni(SO_4)_2.6H_2O$	90	75 000	1·7	29 000	1·7	46 000
$Tl_2Ni(SO_4)_2.6H_2O$	290	80 000	1·7	6 000	1·7	74 000
$(NH_4)_2Ni(SeO_4)_2.6H_2O$	90	76 000	1·7	27 000	1·7	49 000
$NiSO_4.7H_2O$	290	150 000	1·7	60 000	1·7	90 000

Zero field maser properties of some dilute Ni^{2+} and Cr^{2+} salts

are given in free spin units, i.e. as multiples or fractions of the transition probability which a free spin would have if the line width were the same. The data refer to measurements on

75

undiluted salts and the frequencies of the transitions are altered by about 20% on dilution. We can see that $CrSO_4.5H_2O$ appears promising for a 18 000 Mc/s zero field maser. However, both with the Cr^{2+} ion and in particular with Ni^{2+}, the high values of pump frequency required are a disadvantage as power sources in the shorter millimetric wavelength region are not yet easily available. The corresponding properties for diluted crystals containing Fe^{3+} and Gd^{3+} ions are shown in Table 4.3. Both the amplifying and pumping frequencies are

Table 4.3

Ion	Diluent	Temperature of measurement (°K)	Pumping frequency (Mc/s)	Pumping probability for powdered material (free-spin units)	Amplifying frequency (Mc/s)	Amplifying probability for powdered material (free-spin units)	Difference frequency (Mc/s)
Fe^{3+}	$KAl(SeO_4)_2.12H_2O$	20	2 475	0·95	1 020	3·4	1 455
Fe^{3+}	Sapphire	4	31 300	0·02	12 030	5·3	19 270
Fe^{3+}	Cobalt acetyl-acetonate	290	17 000	—	6 000	5	11 000
Gd^{3+}	$Sm_2(SO_4)_2.8H_2O$	290	(a) 14 760	2·4	7 370	17	7 390
			(b) 25 040	0·04	10 280	5	14 760
			(c) 17 670	0·04	7 390	8	10 280

Zero field maser properties of some dilute Fe^{3+} and Gd^{3+} compounds

much lower and so these materials offer much more promise in the centimetric wavelength region where many of the maser's applications lie.

Details of only a few experimental zero field masers have been reported and in these sapphire, Fe^{3+} in Al_2O_3, has been used as the active material. This has an S value of $S = \frac{5}{2}$ giving six levels. King and Terhune (4.13) used a doubly resonant cavity entirely filled with sapphire and by pumping across the $\pm\frac{1}{2}$ to $\pm\frac{5}{2}$ transition at 31·3 kMc/s observed amplification at 12·03 kMc/s from the $\pm\frac{1}{2}$ to $\pm\frac{3}{2}$ transition. At 4·2°K a root gain–bandwidth product of 15 Mc/s was obtained with only 10 mW of pump power.

✳ 4.5 Noise in maser amplifiers

✳ (a) General principles

In maser amplifiers noise radiation arises because of the continual change in population of the energy states of the active material. In calculating the noise due to emission from a material in the emissive state the same approach can be adopted as is used for materials in thermal equilibrium providing that special care is taken in defining temperatures. This Section outlines the steps involved in noise calculations and applies the method to the reflection cavity maser.

We begin by recalling some of the expressions for spontaneous and stimulated emission which occurred in Chapter 1 and rewriting them in Ditchfield's notation (4.14). For a system in thermal equilibrium the black body radiation energy density $U°$ is expressed by Planck's law

$$U° = \frac{8\pi h\nu^3}{c^3[\exp{(h\nu/kT)} - 1]} \qquad (4.29)$$

where h is Planck's constant, ν the frequency of the radiation emitted, c the velocity of light, k Boltzmann's constant and T the absolute temperature. It is often more convenient to use the specific intensity $E°$, defined as the energy radiated per second per frequency interval $d\nu$ within a solid angle $d\Omega$ on an area dA of the substance. The relation between $U°$ and $E°$ is simply

$$U° = \frac{8\pi}{c}E°$$

and so $\qquad E° = \dfrac{h\nu^3}{c^2[\exp{(h\nu/kT)} - 1]} \qquad (4.30)$

Next, consider two energy levels in which in thermal equilibrium the populations in the lower and upper states are $N_1°$ and $N_2°$ respectively. We know that $N_1°$ and $N_2°$ are related by

$$\frac{N_2°}{N_1°} = \exp{(-h\nu/kT)} \qquad (4.31)$$

77

If we now think of a system not in thermal equilibrium, the form of equation (4.31) can be used to define a temperature T_{12} in terms of the population N_1 and N_2 in the lower and upper states of the system. This gives, for T_{12},

$$T_{12} = \frac{h\nu}{k \log_e (N_1/N_2)} \qquad (4.32)$$

The temperature so defined is called the spin temperature of the system. For a system in thermal equilibrium $N_1° > N_2°$ and the spin temperature T_{12} has a positive value equal to the physical temperature T of the system. In a maser, however, a situation exists where $N_2 > N_1$. This is unstable and is maintained (unlike thermal equilibrium) by an outside agency, for example by pumping across other levels. In this case, keeping to the definition, T_{12} is negative. Under these conditions T_{12} is sometimes called a negative spin temperature but it is merely a derived parameter and has no simple relationship to the physical temperature of the material. It has become customary to express thermal radiation in terms of temperature and, by using the idea of a positive or negative spin temperature, the noise power from a maser can be expressed in formulae analogous to those used for a system in thermal equilibrium.

The relation between Johnson noise and thermal radiation in a lumped circuit, such as, for example, a transmission line terminated by a resistance, is obtained by considering the equilibrium between the radiation in an enclosure and the noise power from a resistance coupled to the enclosure. If the noise power P available in a single mode within the frequency interval $d\nu$ comes from a non-reflecting resistance R, it can be shown, by using radiation formulae, that

$$P = \frac{c^2 E°}{\nu^2} d\nu = \frac{h\nu d\nu}{\exp (h\nu/kT) - 1} \qquad (4.33)$$

and by circuit analogies that the mean square noise voltage, $\overline{e^2}$, for a general population is

$$\overline{e^2} = R\frac{h\nu d\nu}{\exp(h\nu/kT) - 1} \qquad (4.34)$$

or

$$\overline{e^2} = R\frac{h\nu}{(N_1/N_2) - 1} \qquad (4.35)$$

In maser terms the resistance R is related to the absorptive loss in the microwave circuit, that is to the reciprocal of the population difference, $R \propto (N_1 - N_2)^{-1}$. Thus the sign of R is the same as that of $(N_1/N_2 - 1)$ and so $\overline{e^2}$ is always positive.

In order to simplify some of the expressions it is convenient now to introduce a symbol ϕ such that

$$\phi = \frac{h\nu}{k(N_1/N_2 - 1)} = \frac{h\nu}{k[\exp(h\nu/kT_{12}) - 1]} \qquad (4.36)$$

We may expand the denominators when $h\nu \ll kT_{12}$ and in this approximation ϕ may be thought of as the temperature T_{12} — it is, however, really related to the noise energy. We know also that the equality of emission and absorption coefficients is a necessary condition for the interchange of energy in equilibrium between radiation and matter and that a good absorber is a good emitter. Therefore, in a complex system, the contribution of each component to the total noise output will be proportional to its value of ϕ and to the extent to which it will absorb power from an electromagnetic field. Thus formulae for reflection, absorption and transmission in each part of the maser system can be used to evaluate the overall noise performance.

✳ (b) *The reflection cavity maser*
Fig. 4.12 shows a schematic diagram of a reflection cavity maser and its signal input waveguide. We can calculate the noise properties of a cavity maser from equivalent circuit analogies. In a reflection cavity maser with only one coupling aperture

at the signal frequency there are two coupling coefficients, β_1 and β_3. The first of these β_1, the coupling coefficient of the cavity input aperture, is the ratio of the power dissipated

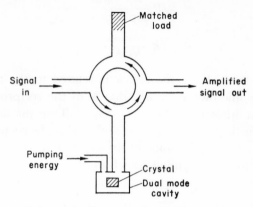

FIG. 4.12   Schematic diagram of reflection cavity maser and signal input waveguide

through this aperture to the power absorbed in the cavity walls. Thus

$$\beta_1 = \frac{Q_u}{Q_i} \tag{4.37}$$

where Q_u is the unloaded cavity Q and Q_i is the Q of the input aperture. The second coefficient β_3 refers to the sample and is defined by

$$\beta_3 = \frac{Q_u}{\lceil Q_m \rceil} \tag{4.38}$$

where Q_m is the magnetic Q of the sample. Thus β_3 is negative when the sample is in an emissive state and has a negative resistance and negative spin temperature.

A reflection cavity maser will usually be used with a circulator and cooled termination as shown in Fig. 4.13. The signal and noise from the aerial or other source are directed into the maser by the circulator. The amplified power from the maser passes to the next stage of the receiver, but noise from the receiver does not reach the maser because it is absorbed in a cooled matched termination. The only noise power passing into the maser from an imperfectly matched aerial is that emitted by the cooled termination and this is usually very

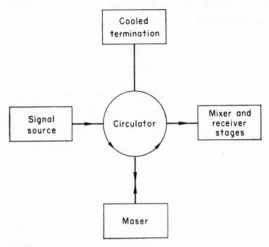

FIG. 4.13   Reflection cavity maser receiver

small. Taking the parameters ϕ_s, ϕ_c and ϕ_m to refer to the source, cavity and maser material respectively, and defining a noise factor F_R as

$$F_R = \frac{\text{input signal/input noise}}{\text{output signal/output noise}}$$

Ditchfield showed that

$$F_R = 1 + \frac{1}{\phi_s}\left(1 - \frac{1}{G}\right)\left(\frac{\phi_c}{|\beta_3| - 1} + \frac{|\phi_m|}{1 - 1/|\beta_3|}\right) \quad (4.39)$$

where G is the power gain in the maser. This shows that the noise properties are determined by the gain, the coupling parameters and the noise energies ϕ_s, ϕ_c and ϕ_m of the source, cavity and material. In everyday terms this means that the maser operating conditions, the cavity design and the choice of maser material influence the noise performance. Most practical

81

masers operate under conditions where $h\nu \ll kT_{12}$ at the signal frequency so that we can replace the ϕ's by corresponding temperatures. It is usually more convenient to work in equivalent noise temperatures rather than noise factors and making this transformation equation (4.39) shows that the input noise temperature of a reflection cavity maser is

$$T_{\text{eff}} = \left(1 - \frac{1}{G}\right)\left(\frac{T_c}{|\beta_3| - 1} + \frac{|T_m|}{1 - 1/|\beta_3|}\right) \quad (4.40)$$

We can again use practical operating criteria to give a much simplified version of equation (4.40). If the amplifier works at high gain the power emitted by the specimen will be large compared with the passive losses in the amplifier and $\beta_3 \gg 1$. In this case

$$T_{\text{eff}} = |T_m| \quad (4.41)$$

i.e. the effective noise input temperature of the cavity maser amplifier is equal to the magnitude of the spin temperature T_m of the amplifying material. This is usually of the order of a few degrees Kelvin. When we compare this with a figure of 3000°K for a high quality conventional superheterodyne receiver we can see immediately why the maser is so important as a microwave amplifier.

✳ (c) Maser receiving systems

We have just seen that the noise temperature of a maser amplifier may be as low as a few degrees Kelvin. In a complete receiver incorporating a maser amplifier there are several other sources of noise each of which may in fact be much larger than that due to the maser. To obtain the overall noise temperature of the complete receiver we must add together the noise contributions from the various parts of the system. In most maser receivers the main noise contributions are due to (1) noise in the source — for example galactic noise, (2) the attenuating medium between the source and the aerial, which is usually the atmosphere, (3) the aerial efficiency, (4) the attenuating transmission lines or waveguides between the aerial and the receiver and (5) the input noise temperature of the maser, which we have just considered. The disposition of these noise sources in a maser receiver system is shown diagrammatically in Fig. 4.14.

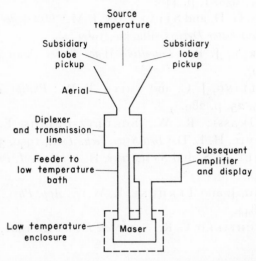

FIG. 4.14   Thermal noise sources in a maser receiving system

As Chapter 6 includes some examples of maser systems in satellite communications and radioastronomy further details are unnecessary here. The important result is that overall system noise temperatures of about 50°K have been achieved.

References

4.1   SCOVIL, H. E. D., FEHER, G. and SEIDEL, H.: *Phys. Rev.*, 1957, **105**, p. 762.

4.2   McWHORTER, A. L. and MEYER, J. W.: *Phys. Rev.*, 1958, **109**, p. 312.

4.3   MORRIS, R. J., KYHL, R. L. and STRANDBERG, M. W. P.: *Proc. I.R.E.*, 1959, **47**, p. 81.

4.4 SINGER, J. R.: *Masers* (Wiley, 1959), p. 102.

4.5 STRANDBERG, M. W. P.: *Phys. Rev.*, 1957, **106**, p. 617.

4.6 SLATER, J. C.: *Microwave Electronics* (Van Nostrand, 1950).

4.7 DITCHFIELD, C. R. and FORRESTER, P. A.: *Phys. Rev. Lett.*, 1958, **1**, p. 448.

4.8 SIMS, G. D. and STEVENSON, I. M.: *Microwave Tubes and Semiconductor Devices* (Blackie, 1963).

4.9 PIERCE, J. R.: *Travelling Wave Tubes* (Van Nostrand, 1950).

4.10 WALLING, J. C. and SMITH, F. W.: *Philips Tech. Rev.*, 1965, **25**, p. 289.

4.11 DEGRASSE, R. W., SCHULTZ-DUBOIS, E. O. and SCOVIL, H. E. D.: *Bell Syst. Tech. Jour.*, 1959, **38**, p. 305.

4.12 BOGLE, G. S. and SYMMONS, H. F.: *Aust. J. Phys.*, 1959, **12**, p. 1.

4.13 KING, J. and TERHUNE, R. W.: *J. App. Phys.*, 1959, **30**, p. 1844.

4.14 DITCHFIELD, C. R.: *Solid State Electronics*, 1962, **4**, p. 171.

*5

Pulsed Solid State Masers

THE simplest energy level scheme we can imagine for a maser is one in which there are just two energy levels. This, as we have seen, was the situation in the gaseous ammonia maser. There are a number of paramagnetic materials (e.g. irradiated calcite and magnesium oxide) in which the paramagnetic centre has an effective spin of $S = \frac{1}{2}$ giving just two energy levels in an external magnetic field. Alternatively, we may think of selecting two of the levels available in any of the multi-level maser materials we have encountered in the previous Chapter. The problem in making a two-level amplifier is of course to invert the population of the two levels chosen. There are three ways in which this can be done, and these are known as field reversal, the 180° pulse technique and adiabatic rapid passage. The first two, field reversal (5.1) and the 180° pulse technique (5.2), are methods which were developed for nuclear magnetic resonance (where relaxation times are relatively long), and have been adapted for electron spin resonance. Neither has proved particularly suitable in making operational two-level maser amplifiers and we shall not discuss them further. However, the third method, adiabatic rapid passage, has been used successfully in a number of centimetric and millimetric maser amplifiers and has also been suggested as the most reliable technique for making measurements of spin-lattice relaxation times. As we shall see any solid state two-level maser must operate in a pulsed manner and this feature has restricted their popularity since at centimetric wavelengths c.w. amplifiers offer more attraction. At millimetric wavelengths, however, the three-level approach runs into difficulties because the pump source must always be at a considerably higher frequency than that of the signal and suitable high power sources are not easily obtainable. It is here perhaps that the two-level maser offers most promise. This Chapter begins by describing the technique of inversion by adiabatic rapid passage and subsequently outlines some of the centimetric and millimetric pulsed maser amplifiers which have been constructed.

5.1 Adiabatic rapid passage

It is convenient to begin by stating what the usual experimental technique is for inverting the population of two levels by adiabatic rapid passage. Imagine a maser crystal placed in a resonant cavity in a magnetic field at low temperature as in a microwave spectrometer. Starting with the magnetic field just below the value for resonance it is swept through resonance to a value just above the resonance value. Simultaneously, a high power pulse of microwave radiation, at the resonance frequency, is applied to the specimen. The sequence of operations is shown in Fig. 5.1. If the sweep rate and the pulse power level are correctly chosen the populations in the two levels are inverted and the system is then capable of emitting stimulated radiation.

We must now see in more detail what is taking place during adiabatic rapid passage and obtain a physical picture by adopting a classical approach (5.3). Suppose that the para-magnetic material is situated in a resonant cavity working in a mode such that the circularly polarized r.f. field H_1 lies in a plane at right angles to the direction of the magnetic field H which is to be swept through resonance. The magnetic moment

us to regard the spins as simply precessing about the direction of the single field H_1, Fig. 5.4. The precession angular velocity ω_p is given by

$$\omega_p = \gamma \mid H_{\text{eff}} \mid \tag{5.5}$$

We can now see how to invert the spin vector. This can be done by changing the direction of the effective field while the

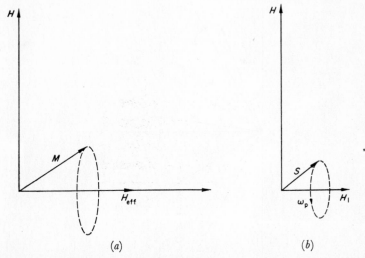

(a)　　　　　　　　　　(b)

FIG. 5.4 (a) Precession of the magnetization vector M about the effective field in a co-ordinate frame rotating at angular velocity giving (b) spin resonance in a rotating frame of reference where $H_{\text{eif}} = H_1$

spin vector precesses about it. Inspection of equation (5.4) shows that there are two ways in which the angle θ' may be altered past 90°. These are, firstly, by changing the value of the large quasi-static field H or, secondly, by altering the frequency ω of the r.f. field. In practice it is easier to alter H by the use of subsidiary modulation coils on the magnet than to frequency sweep the microwave oscillator. This gives the rapid passage sequence we have already outlined. We may imagine that during the rapid passage the spin vector takes up successively the positions indicated in Fig. 5.5.

The adiabatic condition has several implications. In the first place it means that any change of the energy of the system must

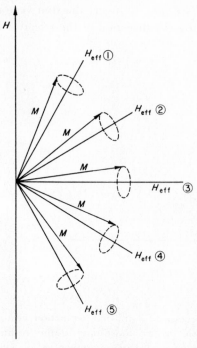

FIG. 5.5 Stages in the course of spin inversion by adiabatic rapid passage using a rotating frame of reference

be made slowly relative to the existing motions in the system. In other words changes in H should be made slowly relative to ω_p. Thus the adiabatic condition becomes

$$\frac{dH}{dt} \ll \omega_p H_1 \tag{5.6}$$

Another requirement is for all the spins to precess about H_{eff} whose magnitude must be larger than that of the local fields due to neighbouring spins, i.e. several times the linewidth. With materials having linewidths of a few oersteds the rate of change of H must usually be less than 10^7 oersteds per second, and suitable sweep rates can readily be obtained by low frequency modulation. There is, however, a lower limit to the modulation frequency, because the inversion must be completed in a time which is short compared with the spin-lattice relaxation time T_1, since otherwise the spin system would return to thermal equilibrium during the rapid passage. In practice this condition does not constitute a severe limitation as there are several materials whose T_1 values are in the millisecond range at liquid helium temperatures; this gives adequate time for inversion to take place.

✳ 5.2 Centimetric two-level masers

Two-level maser amplification has been obtained at centrimetric wavelengths with a number of materials, including single crystals of quartz and magnesium oxide containing paramagnetic defects produced by neutron irradiation (5.4), potassium chromicyanide and ruby. In Chester, Wagner and Castle's experiments the specimens were mounted in a reflection cavity which resonated at 9 kMc/s and had a loaded Q of about 6000 (5.5). Inversion of the spin population was achieved by adiabatic rapid passage in which the magnetic field was swept through the resonance value. Microwave power for the inversion was supplied in $\frac{1}{2}$ watt pulses of duration between 50 μs and 100 μs at a pulse recurrence frequency of 10 c/s. For convenience the inversion and amplification were observed as the magnetic field was swept back through resonance at a controlled delay after the inverting sweep. Under these conditions the duration of the amplifying period was controlled by the rate of the return field sweep. The power reflected from the cavity was monitored with a frequency stabilized c.w. klystron and a superheterodyne receiver. With a quartz specimen containing about 10^{18} spins the inverted state persisted for 2 ms at 4·2°K. Regenerative amplification occurred for times up to 1·2 ms after inversion, the gain decreasing with time. A value of 5×10^6 s^{-1} was obtained for the (gain)$^{\frac{1}{2}}$ bandwidth product with gains between 8 dB and 21 dB. With sufficient inverting power and with or without monitoring power oscillation was observed on the return through resonance. The peak power emitted during oscillation was 12 mW in a pulse of about 10 μs duration. A typical oscillation pulse is shown in Fig. 5.6.

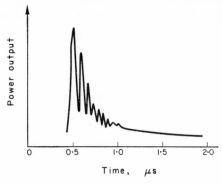

Fɪɢ. 5.6 Two-level quartz maser; waveform of a single pulse emitted from the cavity under oscillation conditions as the magnetic field is swept through resonance after inversion

Similar amplitude modulation has been observed on oscillation pulses from a number of materials and is due to radiation damping in the high Q cavity. After an oscillation pulse amplification was still observed when subsequent field sweeps were applied. The amplification characteristics are illustrated by Fig. 5.7 which shows the result of repeated field sweeps at 130 μs intervals. The wide signal on the left is caused by the inverting pulse. The signal occurring in the second sweep is oscillation. The next eight signals represent amplification each time the field passes through resonance, the gain falling from 16 dB on the third sweep to 6 dB on the seventh and 0 dB on the eleventh.

With a neutron irradiated magnesium oxide single crystal containing 10^{17} spins the inverted state persisted for about 2·5 ms at 4·2°K. Amplification was observed with a gain of 20 dB at 125 μs after inversion, falling to 3 dB after 720 μs.

A two-level solid state maser employing ruby as the paramagnetic material was operated by Hoskins (5.6) at 3 cm

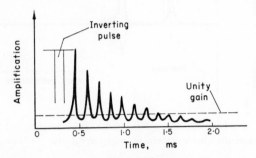

FIG. 5.7 Two-level quartz maser; amplification shown as a function of time after inversion as the magnetic field is swept repeatedly through resonance. Monitoring power 4×10^{-8} watt

wavelengths and liquid helium temperatures. Spin population inversion was easily achieved by sweeping the magnetic field through resonance in about 50 μs while an inverting pulse of microwaves of approximately 500 mW was applied. On returning the magnetic field to the resonance value either oscillation or amplification of a low level monitor signal was observed depending on the size of the inverting pulse, the cavity coupling and the time elapsed after application of the inverting pulse. The repetition rate was limited by the relaxation time to about ten cycles. The crystalline field splitting of the magnetic energy levels inherent in ionic crystals may be used to advantage in reducing the magnetic field requirements for two-level solid state masers. At 3 cm wavelengths, for example, two-level maser operation in ruby was obtained in an external field of only 500 gauss.

We may also notice that inversion by adiabatic rapid passage forms the basis of a technique for measuring spin-lattice relaxation times. This method was used by Chester, Wagner

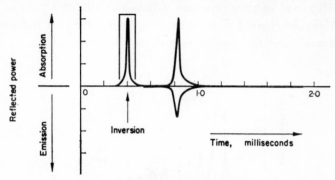

FIG. 5.8 Inversion of a first order line (2–3) in 0·1% Cr potassium chromicyanide using magnetic field sweep

and Castle (5.7) in a study of relaxation processes in dilute potassium chromicyanide. Measurements of relaxation time were made by monitoring the recovery of the whole line with a

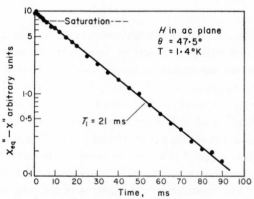

Fig. 5.9 Recovery of a first order line (2–3) in 0.1% Cr potassium chromicyanide after inversion

delayed field sweep after inversion by rapid passage. The form of the oscilloscope presentation, showing the recovered and inverted lines on alternate traces, is shown in Fig. 5.8. The

94

peak-to-peak voltage differences, corrected for instrumental non-linearity, gives directly the deviation from thermal equilibrium. The results obtained in this way for the $-\frac{1}{2}$ to $+\frac{1}{2}$ transition are given in Fig. 5.9 from which we can see that at $1\cdot4°K$ the spin-lattice relaxation time in the $0\cdot001\%$ Cr crystal used was 21 ms. This method for observing relaxation has some advantages over the pulse saturation method in that accurate measurements do not depend so critically on the determination of the reference level corresponding to saturation of the spin system.

✳ 5.3 Millimetric two-level masers

By comparison with the volume of work at centimetric wavelengths there has been relatively little concerned with millimetric maser amplifiers. This is understandable in view of the communications interest in the centimetric wavelength region. There are, however, some special applications (as, for example, in high resolution radar systems, plasma diagnostics and microwave spectroscopy) where millimetric maser amplifiers would be very valuable. One of the few devices on which performance data has been reported is the 8 mm wavelength two-level ruby maser described by Thorp, Pace and Sampson (5.8, 5.9). The salient features of this maser will be outlined because it illustrates both the problems and potentialities of the application of the adiabatic rapid passage technique in the millimetric region. The maser experiments were conducted with a modified 8 mm microwave spectrometer which is shown in diagrammatic form in Fig. 5.10. We may notice that the modifications included the use of a tunable 8 mm power klystron, the provision of a modulating field round the specimen and the addition of a phasing control with which the inverting pulse could be made to occur at any point of the modulation cycle. The modulating field was obtained from a coil mounted between the tails of the inner and outer Dewars; this was cooled in liquid nitrogen

95

and fields of up to 1000 oersteds at frequencies of up to about
1 kc/s could be obtained at the specimen. The low temperature
assembly consisted of a silver-plated cupro-nickel 8 mm waveguide terminated either by a ruby specimen mounted on a

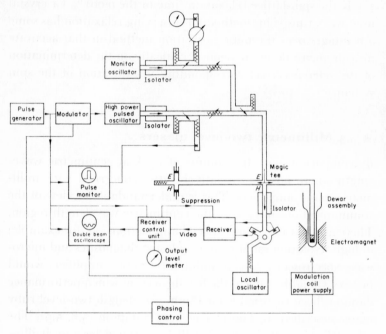

FIG. 5.10   Microwave arrangement for adiabatic rapid
passage at 8 mm wavelengths

plated plunger or by a shaped and silver plated specimen as
shown in Fig. 5.11. These specimens behaved as cavities whose
resonant modes were examined by superposition on the signal
klystron mode pattern, and in this way the frequency, match
and Q factor for each mode was determined.

The timing sequence used to obtain and display rapid
passage inversion patterns was the same as we have illustrated
in Fig. 5.1. In the simplest method of operation both the signal
and inverting klystrons were tuned to the crystal mode selected

and, with the modulating field switched on, the d.c. magnetic field was adjusted for resonance of the transition under study. The inverting pulse was then phased to coincide with an

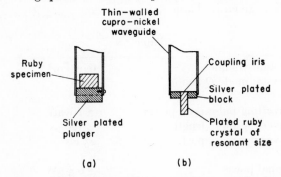

FIG. 5.11   Alternative specimen arrengements for 8 mm
two-level ruby maser

absorption and the inverting pulse power adjusted as required. All the experiments were made with nominal 0·1% Cr ruby using the polar angle $\theta = 90°$ in order to minimize cross

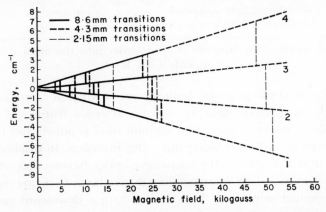

FIG. 5.12   Energy level diagram, for ruby at $\theta = 90°$ showing
8·7 mm, 4·3 mm and 2·1 mm transitions

relaxation and obtain the maximum available spin-lattice relaxation time. The energy level diagram for ruby at $\theta = 90°$ is shown in Fig. 5.12, and we can see that all the 8 mm transi-

97

tions could be examined with the 16 000 oersted field available from the electro-magnet. A set of typical working conditions under which inversion of a first-order transition was observed at 1·4°K is given in Table 5.1.

Table 5.1

Crystal volume	0·03 cm³
Crystal mode Q factor	1000
Inverting pulse peak power	≃ 1 watt
Inverting pulse length	≮ 120 µs
Inverting pulse p.r.f.	25 c/s
Signal power	≃ 0·5 µW
Signal frequency	33·87 Gc/s
D.C. magnetic field	10 425 gauss
Linewidth	20 gauss
Spin-lattice relaxation time	60 ms
Modulating field amplitude	≮ ±100 gauss
Modulating field frequency	500 c/s

Conditions for inversion of a first-order ruby transition at 35 kMc/s, 1·4°K

The inversion patterns obtained, one of which is reproduced in Fig. 5.13, show again the two characteristic features of the two-level maser, namely that amplification is pulsed and that it decreases with increasing time after inversion. In displaying the inversion patterns the microwave bridge balance was set so that the centre line, corresponding to zero input to the receiver, represented saturation. Thus in Fig. 5.13 a downward going signal represents absorption and an upward signal amplification. Since the modulating field frequency was at 500 c/s we can see directly from Fig. 5.13 that some amplification could be obtained for periods of up to about 6 ms after inversion. The gains obtained for the various transitions are given in Table 5.2

which shows that, with an amplifier of this type, the rate of decay of gain with time is sufficiently slow to enable substantially constant gain to be achieved for periods of some tens of micro-

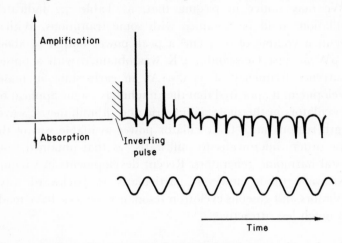

FIG. 5.13 Inversion pattern showing the decrease in gain after application of the inverting pulse. Maximum gain 14 dB, Ruby, $\theta = 90°$, 35 kMc/s, 1·4°K. Timing wave 500 c/s

seconds, a usefully long time in some pulsed microwave systems. Estimates of the bandwidth were made by noting the change in frequency of the signal klystron required to reduce the gain by 3 dB on either side of the maximum. This was

Table 5.2

| Transition | | Gain (dB) during inversion period | | | |
	1 ms	2 ms	3 ms	4 ms	5 ms
1–2	Oscillates	14·2	7·4	5·6	4·1
2–3	11·9	9·7	6·5	3·2	0·5
3–4	3·2	2·2	1·2	0·6	—
1–3	2·4	2·0	1·6	1·2	0·8
2–4	1·4	1·2	1·0	0·7	0·5

Gain at millisecond intervals during inversion period for first- and second-order ruby transitions; $\theta = 90°$, 1·4°K, $Q = 2240$

99

found to be about 10 Mc/s for several transitions giving a root gain–bandwidth product for the maser of about 50 Mc/s at 1·4°K.

We may notice in passing that, as Table 5.2 indicates, oscillation could be obtained with some transitions. With a specimen volume of 0·03 cm³ a peak power output of about 70 μW at 33·1 Gc/s and 1·4°K was obtained with a pulsed recurrence frequency of 25 c/s. At an early stage in maser development it appeared that they might have some application as oscillators in the short millimetric and submillimetric wave-length regions since the oscillator power available was of the same order (microwatts to milliwatts) as that obtained from crystal harmonic generators. Recent developments in vacuum microwave tubes, however, particularly in backward wave oscillators and gaseous cyclotron resonance devices, have made this much less attractive.

References

5.1 PURCELL, E. M. and POUND, R. V.: *Phys. Rev.*, 1951, **81**, p. 279.

5.2 RAMSEY, N. F. and POUND, R. V.: *Phys. Rev.*, 1951, **81**, p. 278.

5.3 SINGER, J. R.: *Masers* (Wiley, 1959).

5.4 WEEKS, R. A.: *J. Appl. Phys.*, 1956, **27**, p. 1376.

5.5 CHESTER, P. F., WAGNER, P. E. and CASTLE, J. G.: *Phys. Rev.*, 1958, **110**, p. 281.

5.6 HOSKINS, R. H.: *J. Appl. Phys.*, 1959, **30**, p. 797.

5.7 CHESTER, P. F., WAGNER, P. E. and CASTLE, J. G.: *Quantum Electronics* (Columbia University Press, 1960), p. 359.

5.8 THORP, J. S.: *Advances in Quantum Electronics* (Columbia University Press, 1961), p. 602.

5.9 THORP, J. S., PACE, J. H. and SAMPSON, D. F.: *J. Elec. and Control*, 1961, **10**, p. 13.

6

Some Maser Applications

THE maser is essentially a microwave amplifier and, as such, we have seen that the bandwidth and gain characteristics which may typically be obtained in cavity and travelling wave masers are very comparable to the corresponding characteristics in more conventional microwave amplifiers such as klystrons and travelling wave tubes. Masers have, however, a unique property, namely their very low noise temperature of a few degrees absolute, which places them in a very advantageous position. Therefore the natural area for their use will be in any system where the signal to be amplified is so weak that the noise generated in conventional amplifiers determines the limit of sensitivity of the system. We must also remember that the power handling capacity of a maser is small, i.e. a maser will saturate at input levels above about 10^{-5} watts, so we think of the primary application as being a low noise r.f. voltage pre-amplifier. There are many instances where the fundamental problem is to pick out a weak signal from noise. Three examples are in satellite communications, radio-astronomy and microwave spectroscopy, where the advent of the maser has helped to make possible either completely new schemes or significant improvements to conventional techniques.

6.1 Masers in satellite communication systems

An artificial earth satellite will, if illuminated by microwave radiation, scatter some of it to a distant receiver in just the same way as does a target in a conventional radar. This enables a communication scheme to be visualized in which the transmitter power is directed at the satellite by a highly directional aerial and part of the energy absorbed and re-radiated by the satellite is collected by a remote receiving station. The basic arrangement for such a scheme is illustrated in Fig. 6.1. In its

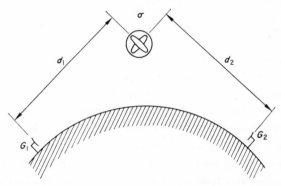

FIG. 6.1   Representation of a satellite communication scheme; σ is the scattering cross-section of the satellite and G_1 and G_2 the aerial gains of the ground stations

simplest form the satellite would be passive, i.e. it would serve merely to scatter some of the incident radiation. This was in fact the arrangement used in the first experiments in communication via artificial earth satellites which were made in 1960 using Echo 1 (6.1).

When we consider the system in a little more detail we quickly realize that the signal reaching the receiver will be very weak. If the transmitting and receiving aerials have gains G_1 and G_2 respectively (referred to isotropic radiators), d_1 and d_2 are the distances from the ground stations to the satellite as shown in Fig. 6.1, λ is the wavelength of the microwave radiation being used and σ is the scattering cross-section of the satellite, calculations which closely follow the derivation of the radar equation show that the total loss L over the path is given by

$$L = \frac{(4\pi)^3 d_1^2 d_2^2}{G_1 G_2 \lambda^2 \sigma} \qquad (6.1)$$

It is instructive to insert into equation (6.1) values for the parameters appropriate to a real situation, and for this purpose, data from the Echo experiment will be used. Here the satellite, a metallized balloon 30 m in diameter, was moving in an almost circular orbit at a height of about 1600 km and had a scattering cross-section of about 730 square metres. Both the transmitting and receiving aerials had gains of about 45 dB at the wavelength of 12·5 cm used, and the ground stations were 4800 km apart. Since the loss L is by definition

$$L = \frac{P_R}{P_T} \qquad (6.2)$$

where P_R and P_T are the received and transmitted powers, it follows that if a 10 kW transmitter is used the received carrier power is only 10^{-14} watts.

This result immediately gives an idea of the role that maser amplifiers play in satellite communications. A signal as low as 10^{-14} watts could very easily be swamped by receiver noise. For example, a good low noise superheterodyne receiver with a bandwidth restricted to 1 Mc/s might have a noise factor of about 1·06 dB, corresponding to a noise temperature of 50°K, and produce an input noise power of 0·7 × 10^{-15} watts. With a carrier signal of only 10^{-14} watts this would give a signal-to-noise power ratio of only 10 dB which would be quite unsatisfactory. The function of the maser therefore is to provide a stage of r.f. pre-amplification which is almost noise-free. In this example the bandwidth has for convenience been taken as 1 Mc/s. In practice a larger bandwidth (up to about 25 Mc/s) is desirable in order to permit the use of as many simultaneous information channels on the one carrier as possible. It is also desirable for a world-wide communication system to have a high altitude satellite in order to obtain longer periods of mutual visibility. These two factors mean that on the one hand the noise will be increased and on the other that the signal is weaker. The latter problem can to some extent be mollified, as in the Telstar experiments (6.2), by using an active satellite, i.e. one which receives the signal from the transmitting station and amplifies it before re-radiating to the receiving station. Notwithstanding this, the signal level reaching the receiver in Telstar experiments at ranges of 10 000 km was only about 10^{-13} watts despite additional improvements in aerial gain. Thus we can see that, at least in satellite communication systems so far envisaged, the maser plays a vital part in the high sensitivity receiver.

In considering in more detail how masers can be used in this way it is helpful to follow Walling and Smith's account (6.3) of the operation of a travelling wave maser at the Communication Satellite Ground Station of the General Post Office at Goonhilly Down, Cornwall. In the receiving system at Goonhilly the aerial is a steerable parabolic antenna 26 m in diameter and the maser amplifier is mounted in a cabin at the back of the antenna. As details of the theory and design of travelling wave masers are given in Chapter 4 only a few operational details of the particular device used here will be mentioned. It is a packaged TW ruby maser (chromium concentration 0·05%) with a signal frequency of 4170 Mc/s — the carrier frequency of the communication system — and a pump frequency of 30 150 Mc/s. Operation at these frequencies requires a magnetic field of 3280 oersteds which is obtained from a permanent magnet. The slow wave structure is of the comb type and uses yttrium iron garnet (YIG) as the isolater material. The packaged nature of the device is shown in Fig. 6.2. The weight and size restrictions imposed by its position on the antenna structure call for particular care in the engineering aspects of the design. We have already seen the use of a permanent magnet instead of a laboratory style electromagnet and we should also take note of the cryogenic engineering both from the point of view of size and reliability and also from that

FIG. 6.2 Travelling wave maser amplifier used at the Communication Satellite Earth Station, Goonhilly Down

of obtaining a low helium evaporation rate. The maser operates at 1·5°K (the pressure over the liquid helium is reduced by pumping with a vacuum pump situated lower down the aerial structure), and by using a large cryostat an operating time of two days can be obtained for every filling of liquid helium.

Table 6.1 gives some performance data for the maser. It has been used both in homogeneous magnetic fields and in specially stepped fields to obtain greater bandwidth. A noise temperature of about 15°K was achieved.

Table 6.1

Operation in a homogeneous magnetic field:	
Electronic gain	52·5 dB
Bandwidth to 3 dB points	16 Mc/s
Total structure forward loss	11 dB
Total structure backward loss	70 dB
Net forward gain	41·5 dB
Noise temperature	15 ± 4°K
Operation in stepped magnetic field ($\Delta H \approx 5 \ Oe$):	
Net forward gain	30 dB
Bandwidth to 3 dB points	28 Mc/s

Performance data of maser used in satellite
communication system

It is worth mentioning some of the operational problems encountered in a system such as this because they are seldom evident in laboratory trials. The chief difficulty was the need for repeated transfers of liquid helium on the site and this reveals the very real need for compact closed cycle liquid helium refrigerator units. A second operational problem was that ambient temperature variations caused sufficient change in the magnetic field of the permanent magnet to alter the maser centre frequency — here the use of a superconducting magnet in the persistent current mode (6.4) seems a possible solution. As regards overall performance, the noise temperature of the first amplifier of the receiver is very significant and we can appreciate the spectacular decrease obtained by comparing the value of 15°K for the maser system with a value of about 900°K corresponding to a good travelling wave vacuum amplifier at the same frequency which would otherwise have had to be used. The maser itself contributed only about 4°K to the overall noise temperature, the remainder arising from the input coaxial cables, microwave components, and sidelobes of the radiation pattern of the antenna. We may reasonably expect improvements to be made in these directions.

6.2 Masers in radio-astronomy

A second field of work in which a major requirement is to identify and analyse a microwave signal whose strength is only of the same order as the noise generated in conventional receivers is in radio-astronomy. This has both similarities to and differences from the communications application we have just discussed. The similarity is that we are thinking of a very sensitive microwave receiving system, so that the receiver would conventionally consist of a large high gain aerial, probably a travelling wave tube amplifier and a superheterodyne receiver. The main differences are, firstly, that the 'transmitter' is a very remote star, radio-star, or galaxy, secondly, that because of the vast distances involved the incoming signals are extremely weak (usually only at or below the noise level of conventional amplifiers) and thirdly, that it is often sufficient to select from the incoming radiation a narrow band of frequencies for examination. These features have several implications both in the design and use of masers to operate with radio-telescopes. One of these is that narrow band cavity masers rather than travelling wave masers can be useful. Another, more exciting from the astronomical point of view, is that, given a certain radio-telescope and receiver combination, the improved signal-to-noise obtainable by the inclusion of a maser pre-amplifier corresponds immediately to greater range potential, i.e. signals might be detectable from sources far more remote than any previously observed.

One of the first applications of a maser as a low noise pre-amplifier used in conjunction with a radio-telescope was in the study of the interstellar hydrogen line (6.5) made by Jelley and Cooper (6.6) with the operational 21 cm maser at Harvard College Observatory. A three-level cavity maser was used and this was mounted at the focus of a 60 ft reflector, just to one side of the antenna feed horn. Some details of the maser cavity arrangements are given in Fig. 6.3. The maser used a 0·05%

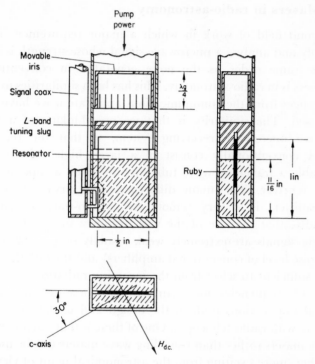

FIG. 6.3   Cavity arrangements in the 21 cm ruby maser

Cr ruby crystal mounted so that the crystalline c-axis was at 90° to the d.c. magnetic field and maintained at 4·2°K. Under these conditions amplification at 1420 Mc/s was obtained with a pump frequency of 11·27 kMc/s in a magnetic field of 2000 oersteds. The latter was obtained from a permanent magnet with trimming coils to give a small amount of tuning. The cavity simultaneously supported the pumping field in an H_{012}

mode and the signal field on a quarter wave strip resonator.
Both the coupling and tuning of the cavity at the signal
frequency were controlled remotely in the observatory building.
The maser was always operated at a gain of 20 dB and a bandwidth of 2 Mc/s. The engineering aspects of the maser again
demonstrate the interplay between environment and design.

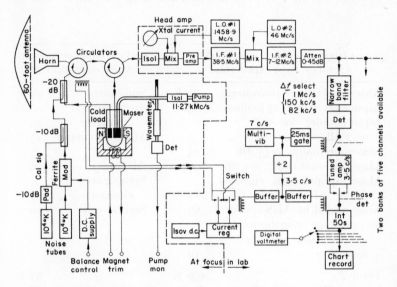

FIG. 6.4   Component layout of 21 cm ruby maser radiometer

Thus, because it was to be mounted at the focus of the aerial,
the overall weight of the maser unit was restricted to 200 lb,
the cryostat arrangements enabled sixteen hours operation to
be obtained per helium filling, and particular attention was
paid to the rigidity of the unit because unusual strains and
angles of tilt occurred as the steerable telescope was moved and
deviations of crystal alignment of as little as half a degree
halved the gain.

The maser unit formed part of the complete radiometer
receiver shown in diagrammatic form in Fig. 6.4; an automatic

gain stabilization (AGS) system was incorporated. The maser unit was first used as a total power radiometer and later as a Dicke comparison radiometer with a switched circulator. (For more details of radiometers and the measurement of thermal radiation at microwave frequencies see Dicke, 6.7.) It is interesting to see how the overall noise temperatures of the two systems accrue. This is shown in Table 6.2. We can see that in

Table 6.2

Original system (with AGS) October 1959–April 1960		Dicke comparison system April 1960–Present	
Antenna spillover (measured)	20°K	Spillover	20°K
Input coax. cable (1⅝ in diam.)	<4	Switched	
Input coupler (for AGS,		circulator	25
0·07 dB)	5	Maser circulator	25
Maser circulator (0·35 dB)	25		
Maser cryostat coax. (0·1 dB)	7	All cables	15
Maser spontaneous emission		Spontaneous	
(theor.)	~2	emission	2
Noise added by AGS system	63	Second stage	10
Second-stage contribution, (20-dB maser gain, on 1000°K)	10		
Total T_N	136°K		97°K

Noise temperatures of 21 cm maser radio-telescope components

the first system the noise temperature due to the maser crystal itself is only 2°K out of a total of 136°K. The major contributions to noise were from the antenna spillover, the maser circulator and, by far the worst source, the automatic gain stabilization system. In the second arrangement the maser again contributes 2°K, but the radiometer losses have been substantially reduced giving a total of 97°K. The importance of these figures lies in the comparison with the noise temperature of the original radiometer system prior to the installation of the maser. This was 1000°K so we can see that the inclusion of the maser pre-amplifier resulted in an improvement of sensitivity by a factor of 10. The minimum integration time to detect a marginal signal was also reduced in this case by a

Table 6.3

Object NGC number	Hubble type	Approximate spectral width (kc/s)	ΔT_H HI emission (°K)	ΔT_c continuum (°K)
55	Sc	900	0·8	⩽0·03
10	Sc	400	0·4	⩽0·03
247	Sc	1000	0·1	⩽0·03
253	Sc	—	<0·15	0·3
300	Sc	725	0·8	0·05
1613	Irregular	120	1·0	—
Holmberg II	Irregular	500	0·3	⩽0·05
3109	Irregular	600	0·5	⩽0·04
Sextans A	Dwarf irr.	300	0·2	⩽0·03
2574	Irregular	600	0·2	⩽0·04
4214	Irregular	300	0·3	⩽0·03
4258	Sb	900	0·05	0·08
4449	Irregular	600	0·3	⩽0·04
4486	Ep	—	<0·2	10·3
4631	Sc	1400	0·2	0·09
4656	Irregular	700	0·2	⩽0·04
4736	Sb	500	0·1	⩽0·05
5236	Sc	800	0·3	0·14
6946	Sc	800	0·2	0·09

Interstallar hydrogen line data obtained with a maser radio-telescope

factor of 100. Some of the data obtained in hydrogen line studies of galaxies is tabulated in Table 6.3. For each of the galactic sources listed in column one measurements were made of the linewidth of the hydrogen line emission, of the antenna temperature due to hydrogen line emission (ΔT_H, column 4),

and of the antenna temperature due to any co-existent con-
tinuum radiation from the source (ΔT_c, column 5). The
sensitivity of the equipment was such that the r.m.s. fluctuation
noise levels on the values of ΔT_H, and ΔT_c were only about
0·03°K.

A second example of the use of masers in radio-astronomy
is the x-band ruby maser radiometer developed by Bair, Cook,
Cross and Arnold at the University of Michigan (6.8). The
radiometer system uses a four-level push–pull ruby cavity
maser pre-amplifier (cf. Section 4.2) and is installed on an
85 ft paraboloidal antenna. The main operating characteristics
of the maser unit are given in Table 6.4. An overall system

Table 6.4

Signal frequency		8·72 Gc/s
Pump frequency		22·4 Gc/s
Magnetic field		3850 Oe
Polar angle θ		55° 44′
Maser gain		20–23 dB
Gain–bandwidth product		300 Mc/s
System bandwidth (IF limited)		8 Mc/s
Maser gain stability		
Short term	<10 mins	0·6%
	<30 mins	2·0%
Long term	>30 mins	5·0%

Operating characteristics of x-band ruby maser radiometer

noise temperature of less than 60°K was obtained (excluding
the antenna temperature), and the r.m.s. values of noise
fluctuation with a 12-second integration time were less than
0·02°K. We should notice particularly that the sensitivity of
the maser radiometer coupled with the low system noise temperature enabled peak-to-peak signal-to-noise ratios of 2 to 1

to be obtained for a 0·10°K source with reasonably short integration times of 12 seconds. A very great amount of astronomical research is made possible with a system which performs suitably with time constants of 12 seconds or less because more averaging and complex drift curve analysis is not necessary.

We can very readily see the advantage of the inclusion of the maser in the radiometer by making a visual comparison between the drift curves shown in Fig. 6.5. These are of Cassiopeia A, a standard radio-astronomical source of relatively high intensity. Curve (a) shows the clean signal obtained with the maser pre-amplifier and curve (b) the corresponding result obtained with the same system but with the maser switched off. Here the maser gain was only 17 dB, and in the taking the second drift curve the I.F. gain was increased to balance the loss of the maser gain.

Even more striking were the results obtained from a much weaker source, Tycho Brahe's supernova, using a higher maser gain. These are reproduced in Fig. 6.6. In this figure curve (a) also shows the signal obtained with the maser pre-amplifier and curve (b) without the maser, and we can see that the improvement is very marked. Bair, et al., also reported the first radio detection of the planet Saturn. On the first occasion seven drift curves were obtained, each of which showed positive and unambiguous detection of radio emission at the planet's predicted position. A second set of drift curves were taken five days later to eliminate the possibility of confusion with other extraterrestrial sources. Data from the combined results are shown in Fig. 6.7. When the second set of observations were made the predicted change in Saturn's right ascension was 37·3 seconds westward as compared with the measured value of 36·5 ± 2 seconds westward. From the measurements, the average value of peak antenna temperature was estimated as 0·095 ± 0·02°K, and this indicated that the equivalent black body disc temperature of Saturn was 106 ± 21°K.

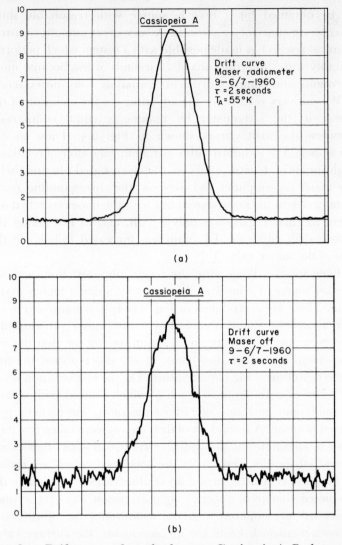

FIG. 6.5 Drift curves of standard source Cassiopeia A. Both curves were obtained with the same system except that (b) has the maser off and its gain replaced by IF gain. $\tau = 2$ seconds, $T_A \sim 35°$ K, $\lambda = 3·45$ cm; (a) with maser pre-amplifier, (b) without maser pre-amplifier

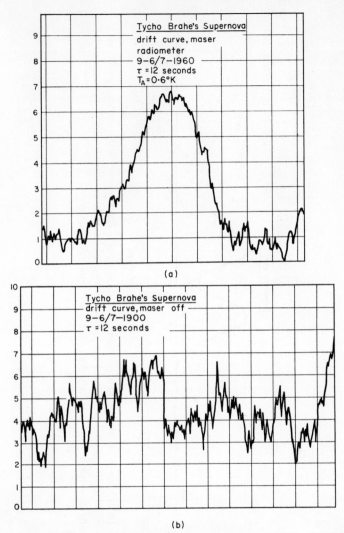

(a)

(b)

FIG. 6.6 Drift curves of Tycho Brahe's Supernova IAU: OON6A. Both curves obtained with the same system except that (*b*) has the maser off and its gain replaced by IF gain. $\tau = 12$ seconds. Arrow indicates source position in (*b*). $T_A = 0\cdot6^\circ$ K, $\lambda = 3\cdot45$ cm. (*a*) with maser pre-amplifier, (*b*) without maser pre-amplifier

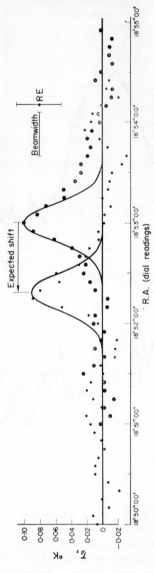

FIG. 6.7 Drift curves of planet Saturn taken five days apart. Each curve is the average of seven individual drift curves. Solid lines are Gaussian representation at the expected average shift in right ascension. $\lambda = 3\cdot45$ cm. August 25–26, 1960, August 30–31

116

✳ 6.3 Masers and microwave spectroscopy

Having mentioned in the preceding sections two systems involving the use of maser pre-amplifiers, a laboratory situation where there is an equal need for low noise amplification at microwave wavelengths should be considered. This is in the field of microwave resonance and in particular electron spin resonance. The situation arises due to causes different from those encountered before and is related to the factors which determine the signal strength in a microwave spectrometer.

In a conventional spectrometer the specimen is mounted in a resonant cavity and a reflection method is used with a bridge circuit to balance out the standing reflection from the cavity. The signal strength then depends primarily upon the input power level, the total attenuation in the system, the number of spins present in the specimen and the transition probability for the resonance under investigation. This signal strength will usually be small, and in practice the sensitivity limit is often determined by the noise in the amplifier stages, whether super-heterodyne or phase-sensitive detection is used. If experiments are conducted to look, for example, at normally forbidden resonance lines, to study detailed lineshapes in the tails of absorption lines, to investigate pair spectra or to detect a very small number of spins, the familiar problem to identifying a signal well hidden by noise arises. It is in this kind of situation that masers offer a means of improving matters.

This possibility is well known but surprisingly there have been few reports of practical equipments. Most attempts were based on the use of three-level solid state masers because of their bandwidth (typically about 2 Mc/s), and the relatively high power (10^{-5} W) which could be handled before saturation occurred. Gambling and Wilmhurst (6.9), however, have described an electron spin resonance spectrometer using an ammonia maser as a pre-amplifier at 23 kMc/s. They point out that, as the sensitivity of a spectrometer increases with frequency

f as $f^{\frac{1}{2}}$ for a constant filling factor, a maser operating at 23 Mc/s is more useful than the normal three-level maser which typically operates at or below 10 kMc/s.

In Gambling and Wilmhurst's system, Fig. 6.8, the arrange-

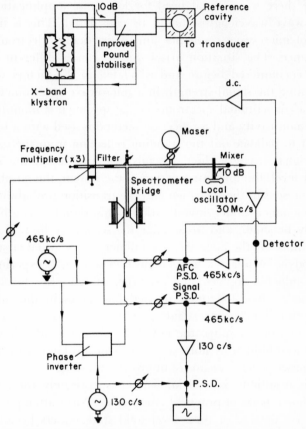

FIG. 6.8 Schematic diagram of a 23 kMc/s electron spin resonance spectrometer incorporating an ammonia maser pre-amplifier

ment is basically that of a conventional superheterodyne spectrometer. An ammonia maser, however, is coupled into the waveguide between the microwave bridge and the mixer. We should notice the additional circuitry and techniques adopted to avoid saturating the maser, whose saturation level is only about 10^{-12} W, and to keep the electron spin resonance signal within its 300 c/s passband. The primary source of microwave power was an X-band klystron and the 23 kMc/s radiation was generated by using a $\times 3$ frequency multiplier. This technique enabled better stabilization to be obtained, using an improved Pound (6.10) stabilizer at X-band, than would have been possible in a corresponding K-band system. Automatic frequency control (AFC) was also provided to overcome long-term drift in the Pound stabilizer. For this the K-band carrier was amplitude modulated at 465 kc/s by feeding a 465 kc/s signal to the frequency multiplier. The frequency of one of the sidebands produced was adjusted (by altering the carrier frequency) to the maser frequency and was amplified. The 465 kc/s output from the spectrometer was fed to a phase-sensitive detector (P.S.D.) which was set to give zero output when the sideband frequency corresponded exactly to the centre of the maser response. A d.c. error signal was produced when the sideband frequency drifted and this, after amplification, actuated a piezo-electric transducer which deformed the wall of the reference cavity. The modulating signal at 465 kc/s, chosen to be high compared with the 7 kc/s natural linewidth of the ammonia inversion resonance, was also fed to the magnet. This enabled one of the sidebands to be amplified when the carrier was tuned 465 kc/s away from the maser frequency and so provided adequate protection from saturation. The signal at 465 kc/s from the frequency stabilization loop is, in this arrangement, superimposed on the electron spin resonance signal and the separation of the two is achieved by inverting the 465 kc/s modulating field at 130 c/s from a separate 130 c/s source. The spectrometer output consists of a 130 c/s signal which is fed to a 130 c/s phase-sensitive detector before display.

The equipment was used in studies of spin resonance in carbon. We can see the improvement in sensitivity from the displays of Fig. 6.9, which show corresponding spectra from a small specimen of carbon obtained with and without the maser pre-amplifier. A gain of 17 dB was obtained by using the maser and, with K-band generator power of about 30 μW, no increase in noise level was detectable on amplification. In terms of ability to detect a small number of spins this performance represented an improvement in sensitivity of about 10 dB over standard commercial e.s.r. spectrometers.

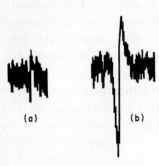

(a)   (b)

FIG. 6.9 Absorption spectra of carbon specimen (a) without maser pre-amplification, (b) with maser pre-amplification

We may notice also that, as regards the availability of wave-guide components, K-band (necessary for the operation of the ammonia maser) is not so well developed as either X-band (3·2 cm) on the longer wavelength side or Q-band (8·6 mm) on the shorter wavelength side. We may reasonably expect further improvements in spectrometer techniques as solid state masers become more widely used, particularly if it becomes possible to obtain a wider frequency coverage with 77°K masers.

References

6.1   *Bell System Tech. Jour.*, 1961, **40**.
6.2   *Bell System Tech. Jour.*, 1961, **42**.
6.3   WALLING, J. C. and SMITH, F. W.: *Philips Tech. Rev.*, 1965, **25**, p. 289.
6.4   CIOFFI, P. P.: *J. Appl. Phys.*, 1962, **33**, p. 875.
6.5   EWAN, H. I. and PURCELL, E. M.: *Nature*, 1951, **168**, p. 356.

6.6 JELLEY, J. V. and COOPER, B. F. C.: *Advances in Quantum Electronics* (Columbia University Press, 1961), p. 619.

6.7 DICKE, R. H.: *Rev. Sci. Inst.*, 1946, **17**, p. 268.

6.8 BAIR, M. E., COOK, J. J., CROSS, L. G., and ARNOLD, C. B.: *I.R.E. Trans. on Antennas and Propagation*, 1961, **AP-9**, p. 43.

6.9 GAMBLING, W. A. and WILMHURST, T. H.: *Physics Letters*, 1963, **5**, p. 228.

6.10 POUND, R. V.: *Proc. I.R.E.*, 1947, **35**, p. 1405.

7

Population Inversion at Optical Frequencies

In the microwave region, which was considered in Chapter 3, we found that the useful energy level systems were confined to those of two classes of material, i.e. certain gaseous molecules and, in the main, paramagnetic single crystals. At optical frequencies the choice is by no means so restricted and consequently there is a greater variety of methods for obtaining inverted populations. The four main classes of laser so far developed utilize, as active materials, paramagnetic single crystals, gaseous mixtures, semiconducting compounds and fluorescent liquids respectively. We can in many instances retain the principle of three-level operation, provided that intermediate states are allowed to participate in setting up an inverted population across the laser transition. Hence we can employ many of the ideas introduced in the microwave regime. In doing so, however, we must be careful to realize that the experimental equipment may be quite different since optical rather than microwave techniques are applicable. In the gaseous mixture and semiconductor lasers, however, there are some pumping schemes which do not have direct counterparts in microwave region. This Chapter outlines the principles of some of these laser pumping schemes, leaving the details of the corresponding experimental designs and techniques for discussion in Chapters 8, 9 and 10.

7.1 Optical spectra of some paramagnetic ions

One of the earliest solid materials to be used for lasers was ruby, Cr^{3+} in Al_2O_3 (Maiman, 7.1), which we have already met as a maser material. Ruby forms a convenient first example to indicate which energy levels are involved at optical fre-

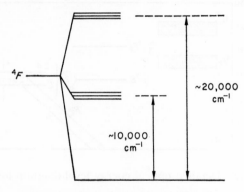

FIG. 7.1   The optical levels in ruby

quencies and how an inverted population may be obtained. Fig. 7.1 reproduces the part of Fig. 3.1 which is relevant to optical frequencies, namely the orbital levels whose lowest member lies some 10^4 cm^{-1} above the ground state. The energy differences between these orbital levels and the ground state correspond to transitions at optical frequencies. It is therefore among these that the search for a suitable system must be conducted.

The orbital levels are shown in more detail in Fig. 7.2 and we should notice that these are levels determined by the ion (Cr^{3+}) and the lattice (Al_2O_3) in the absence of any magnetic field. We can see by comparison the very small splittings of the spin levels used in the microwave region. In the optical spectra there is a broad band, level 3, ($^4F_2$), about 17 000 cm^{-1} above the ground state. There is also a pair of sharp fluorescent lines, level 2, (^2E), which lies nearly 15 000 cm^{-1} above the ground state. The $^4F_2$ band and the ^2E levels are coupled, and phonon assisted transitions can take place between them so that any population change occurring in the $^4F_2$ band is transferred as a corresponding change to the ^2E levels, which have long lifetimes of about 3 ms at room temperature. With these levels

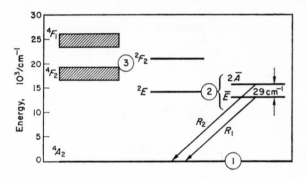

FIG. 7.2   Detailed optical energy level diagram for ruby

laser operation can be obtained by pumping the 1–3 transition with green light. This sets up an inverted population across levels 2 and 1, resulting in stimulated emission of radiation from the laser transitions between the ^2E levels and the ground state — ordinarily emission takes place from the lower fluorescent level only at a wavelength of 6943 Å in the red region of the visible spectrum, the R_1 line.

Although these examples refer to optical transitions and lifetimes the theory of Chapter 1 holds, and in order to optimize the coherent laser output the crystal must be placed in an optical resonator. Details of some of these are given later but, for solid materials, some form of Fabry–Perot interferometer is usually employed, while for gases confocal mirror arrangements are often more suitable. The fluorescent linewidth is about 3 Å, but under the oscillation conditions of laser operation this can be reduced to as little as about 5×10^{-4} Å corresponding to an extremely monochromatic, coherent light beam. The emission wavelength varies with the temperature of the crystal, however, simply because thermal expansion or contraction of the lattice affects the energy level spacings. The wavelength variation for ruby has been estimated as

$$\lambda(T) = 6943 \cdot 25 + 0 \cdot 068(T - 20) \qquad (7.1)$$

where, in this particular instance, T is the temperature in degrees Centigrade (Abella and Cummins, 7.2). We can already see two major differences emerging between masers and lasers — in the latter, with this type of crystal, there is no need for a magnetic field and, if the aim is to generate a coherent light beam rather than obtain low noise amplification, there is also no fundamental requirement for very low temperatures.

Several other materials form useful host lattices for laser crystals. The primary requirement is for combinations of ion and host lattice each of which gives a laser transition at a different point of the optical spectrum since each particular laser crystal gives an essentially monochromatic source. Calcium fluoride, CaF_2, is one alternative lattice. Stimulated emission from uranium in calcium fluoride (U^{3+} in CaF_2) was observed in 1960 (Sorokin and Stevenson, 7.3). The energy level scheme is shown in Fig. 7.3 and the laser transition occurs at $2 \cdot 613$ microns with pumping in the $0 \cdot 88$ to $0 \cdot 92$ micron range. Samarium-doped calcium fluoride (Sm^{2+} in CaF_2), when pumped in a broad band from $0 \cdot 3$ to $0 \cdot 6$ micron, gives a laser transition at $0 \cdot 70$ micron. The neodymium ion Nd^{3+} gives several useful laser transitions in different lattices. In calcium fluoride there is a laser transition at $1 \cdot 046$ microns, while in calcium tungstate, Nd^{3+} in $CaWO_4$, there is a strong transition at $1 \cdot 06$ microns, Fig. 7.4 (Carlson and Dieke, 7.4). Laser action has also been reported with Nd^{3+} in barium glass (Snitzer, 7.5).

This is an interesting host material because there is the possibility of obtaining better doping uniformity and optical perfection in a glass than in a synthetic single crystal.

In all these solid state examples optical pumping is used
though at a variety of frequencies. It should be mentioned here

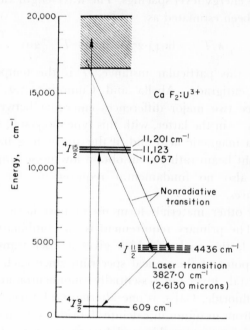

FIG. 7.3   Energy level system for U^{3+} in CaF_2, showing
2·61 μ laser transition

that this is achieved by directing the light output of a flash
tube on to the laser crystal. The pumping source can be fairly
wide-band because we are pumping from the ground state into
a band and input energies over a considerable wavelength
range all contribute to the inversion. In principle the multi-
level solid state laser materials would support continuous laser
operation if the optical pump power were supplied continuously. In practice, as explained in more detail in Chapter 8,

difficulties are encountered because, firstly, high power continuously operated flash tubes are not readily available and,
secondly, heat dissipation problems in the laser crystal become
serious.

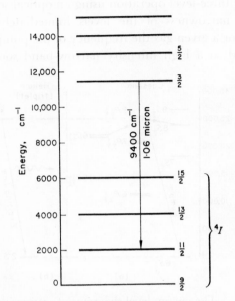

FIG. 7.4   The 1·06 μ laser transition of Nd^{3+} in calcium tungstate

7.2 Inversion in gaseous systems

The spectra of gases provide an abundant source of laser
emission lines. In these, however, the energy levels are narrow
and the broad bands characteristic of the solids are absent.
This leads to difficulties in excitation because a means of
pumping in a narrow bandwidth is necessary. There is one
example, the caesium laser, in which levels of the caesium ion
are utilized directly in the same sense as for solids and narrow-
band optical pumping is employed to obtain an inverted population across the laser transition. In the remainder inversion is
obtained by utilizing collision processes in gas mixtures.

(a) Direct optical absorption

The spectra of the free atoms in a gas are much simpler than those found in solids and consist of sets of narrow levels. In considering three-level operation using an optical source as the pump the narrowness of the levels immediately creates a problem. For a given gas the frequency of the pump transition is fixed and so a high intensity narrow-band source at this

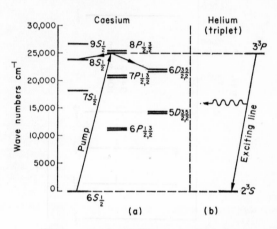

FIG. 7.5   The energy level diagrams of (a) caesium and (b) helium

particular frequency would be required. (This is, of course, just the situation we have met in pumping across spin levels in microwave masers. Here, however, klystrons form pumping sources and with the frequency coverage of the range of valves available essentially monochromatic outputs are obtainable at most wavelengths in the centimetric band.)

  There are two ways in which atoms can be excited across the pumping levels. The first is by absorption of the emission line of the same levels and the second is by absorption of an emission line of another element which has the same wavelength, a very rare occurrence. The former scheme was proposed by Schawlow and Townes (7.6) for exciting a potassium vapour laser, but has not so far been successful. The latter has been used in the particular case of the caesium laser (Jacobs, Gould and Rabinowitz, 7.7). The energy levels of caesium are shown in Fig. 7.5 (*a*) and if we compare these with the spectra of helium, Fig. 7.5 (*b*), we can see that the wavelength of the helium emission line (3^3p–2^3s) is almost exactly the same as that of the ($6s_{\frac{1}{2}}$–$8p_{\frac{1}{2}}$) transition in caesium, (3889·69 Å and 3889·67 Å respectively). In the caesium laser a helium discharge lamp was used to generate narrow-band radiation centred at 3889·69 Å and this was used to irradiate a tube containing caesium vapour. This gave very efficient pumping and continuous laser amplification and oscillation were observed at 7·18 μ. Despite its high efficiency, however, the method is only of limited applicability because there are very few examples of suitable coincidences in wavelength of emission and absorption lines.

(*b*) *Collison processes in gaseous mixtures*

A more widely applicable method for obtaining an inverted population is to use excitation by collision in a gas mixture. Several concepts are involved in this.

If an electrical discharge is maintained in a gas at low pressure electrons are formed. These accelerate in the field and so acquire energies which, in a steady discharge, follow a Maxwell–Boltzmann distribution. The energies of the electrons can thus be represented by a temperature, the electron temperature T_e, which is characteristic of the distribution. Inelastic collisions may occur between electrons and atoms but in these the atoms can only gain or lose amounts of energy consistent with their energy level schemes. According to this the atoms would then be distributed among their energy levels such that the number N_n in the nth state would be

$$N_n = N_1 \exp\left[-\left(\frac{E_n - E_1}{kT_e}\right)\right] \tag{7.2}$$

where N_1 is the number of atoms in the ground state and E_n and E_1 are the energies of the upper and ground states.

This distribution is not in fact taken up because two effects cause perturbations. The first is that, as a result of inter-atomic and electron-atom collisions, some excitation energy is lost as kinetic energy so that the atomic temperature T_a is less than the electron temperature T_e. The second, more significant effect is that radiative transitions take place so that the excited atoms pass to lower energy states. Thus in a gas atoms may be excited either by collisions in which they gain energy from electrons (collisions of the first kind) or by absorbing radiation. Atoms may be de-excited by collisions in which they lose energy to electrons (collisions of the second kind) by spontaneous emission of radiation or by stimulated emission of radiation.

These processes compete and a stationary situation will be established in which the rate of arrival of atoms in a given state (due to all causes) is just balanced by the rate of departure. This balance can be described by sets of rate equations (Basov and Krokhin, 7.8, Lengyel. 7.9), and we find that the number of atoms in each state is adjusted to suit the balancing condition. In consequence atoms will accumulate in any states which have long lifetimes associated with them. They are called metastable states, an example being the lowest triplet state of a gas whose ground state is a singlet.

In principle then an inverted population between a metastable state and a lower level may be obtained by electronic collision processes in a single gas. Laser action has been produced in this way in the pure rare gases. In each of these the number of laser transitions is quite large and covers a wide range of wavelength. Direct excitation takes place between the ground state to s levels, but many of the longer wavelength emission lines observed in the laser spectra correspond to transitions between d and p levels.

A more general method, and one widely used in practical gas lasers, is to obtain inverted populations by electronic collisions in gas mixtures. The new feature here is that energy may be exchanged between colliding atoms of different elements providing that they have a pair of almost identical energy levels.

The first system in which this mechanism was shown to work was a helium–neon mixture (Javan, Bennett and Herriott, 7.10). The relevant parts of the energy level diagrams of helium and neon are shown in simplified form in Fig. 7.6. In helium

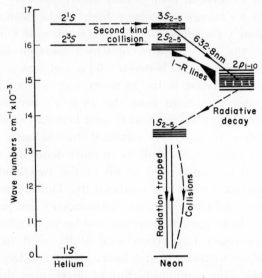

FIG. 7.6   The helium–neon energy level system

the ground state is a singlet and the 2^3S state is a metastable state from which direct radiative transitions to the ground state are forbidden. If a discharge is set up in the gas, however, atoms can be excited into the 2^3S state by electronic collisions of the first kind. The $2S$ levels of neon lie at very nearly the same energy above the ground state as does the 2^3S state of helium and thus excited helium atoms, after collision with neon atoms in the ground state, can transfer their energy to neon atoms thereby exciting them to the $2S$ levels. Thus an excess population can be built up in the $2S$ levels of neon. The probability ω_{ex} of the energy exchange process taking place depends on the energy difference ΔE between the two energy levels involved and

$$\omega_{ex} = \text{constant} \times \exp^{(-\Delta E/kT)} \tag{7.3}$$

where T is the gas temperature. In the helium–neon mixture the energy difference between the 2^3S state in helium and the uppermost $2S$ level in neon is only about 300 cm^{-1}, and the probability for energy exchange is high. In the neon spectrum the selection rules allow thirty laser transitions between $2S$ levels and the ten $2p$ states, of which fourteen have been observed at wavelengths between 0·63 μ and 1·52 μ (Bennett, 7.11). The population in the $2p$ states does not build up as a result of laser transitions from the $2S$ levels because the $2p$ states couple to the lower $1S$ levels and hence to ground state.

The degree of inversion obtained by exchange collision processes depends, as we shall see in more detail in Chapter 9, on the relative numbers of atoms of the two kinds in the mixture and on the electron temperature. This means that the gas pressure and the discharge characteristics are parameters which must be controlled in operational lasers. Similar electron collision processes have been successfully used in a large number of gas mixtures to give laser action at widely different wavelengths. One common feature of lasers using this type of pumping scheme is that they can be operated continuously since it is quite easy to maintain a continuous discharge in a gas mixture.

7.3 Inversion in semiconductors

Semiconducting materials form a third distinct class of materials in which laser action may be obtained. These materials are used in solid form but discussion of their energy levels must be conducted in terms of bands rather than the discrete levels obtained with, for example, paramagnetic single crystals. In several semiconducting materials the energy gap between the valence band and the conduction band, Fig. 7.7, corresponds to optical wavelengths. Furthermore, holes and electrons present in the semiconductor may recombine emitting the re-combination radiation observed with many semiconducting materials. Thus semiconductors are potentially useful laser materials provided, firstly, that radiative recombination pre-dominates over other non-radiative decay processes and,

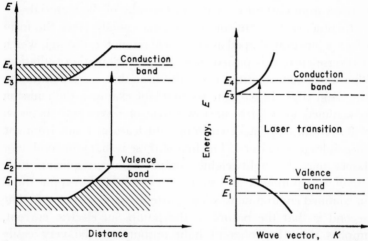

FIG. 7.7   Band structure of semi-conductor laser material

FIG. 7.8   *E–K* diagram for a semiconductor laser material

secondly — as always in obtaining stimulated emission — that an excess population can be maintained across the laser transition.

The first of these requirements largely determines which semiconductors may be used because the transition probability for a radiative transition across the gap must be high and must exceed the probabilities for non-radiative transfer of energy to the lattice or to other free holes or electrons. This condition corresponds to a situation on the energy–wave vector diagram, Fig. 7.8, in which the maximum energy of the valance band and the minimum energy of the conduction both appear at a wave vector value of zero. Under these circumstances transitions across the gap are allowed and the transition probability can be high. This situation arises in gallium arsenide and indium antimonide. The second requirement, that of maintaining an adequate population difference across the gap, is relatively easy to meet by carrier injection, the 'pumping source' becoming simply a current passing through the semiconductor. Effectively the system forms a two-level device in which the normal population distribution can be inverted by the injection of carriers from current contacts on the sides of the material.

In practice the semiconductor laser usually takes the form of a p–n junction, shaped as an optical resonator, through which a reverse current is passed to obtain recombination radiation. The wavelength emitted is usually near that corresponding to the band edge. In gallium arsenide, for example, the emission is confined to a fairly narrow range of wavelength between 8380 Å and 8392 Å. Two important features result from the principles just outlined. The first of these is that semiconductor lasers may be lightweight, compact units requiring little auxiliary equipment and so are very suitable for applications in confined environments such as satellites and space-craft. The second is that the nature of the pump, an electric current, implies that the coherent light output may be very easily modulated by modulating the current passing through the semiconductor, an attractive feature for communication systems.

7.4 Optical resonators

There is a considerable difference between the closed metallic cavity resonators which we use at microwave frequencies and their optical analogues. The former, of course, support several modes but, because the microwave cavity has dimensions of the same order as the guide wavelength, the modes are well separated in frequency and we can normally regard the cavity as resonating only at the signal frequency required. Further, radiation cannot escape from the cavity except via the coupling loop or iris. In the optical region, however, the resonator dimensions may be as much as 10^5 times greater than the wavelength, and so a large number of closely spaced resonances may be involved.

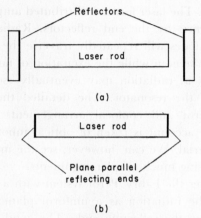

(a)

(b)

FIG. 7.9 The Fabry–Perot optical resonator (a) with separate reflectors, (b) with reflectors deposited on laser crystal

Two types of optical resonator are in common use. The first is based on the Fabry–Perot interferometer. The laser material, usually in rod form, is either placed between external plane parallel reflecting plates, Fig. 7.9 (a), or may itself form an interferometer by having its ends ground parallel, polished and silvered, Fig. 7.9 (b). The second type of resonator is based on the confocal mirror arrangement, Fig. 7.10, in which the laser

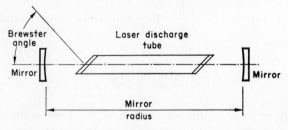

FIG. 7.10 The confocal optical resonator, showing Brewster angle windows terminating a gas laser discharge tube

material is placed between two identical spherical mirrors separated by a distance equal to their common radius of curvature.

We can see immediately that the optical resonators are not closed systems. The laser forms a distributed amplifier within a resonator defined by the end reflectors. Radiation confined within axial modes will repeatedly traverse the specimen and contribute to the gain while the excitation of non-axial modes represents loss as radiation may eventually escape from the open sides of the resonator. The detailed theories of both the Fabry–Perot and confocal arrangements are complex, particularly if account is taken of optical inhomogeneities in the laser material. We can, however, see the main features of their action using much simpler arguments.

First consider the Fabry–Perot system with a solid laser rod and regard the radiation as a uniform plane wave passing axially between the reflecting ends. The condition for resonance is that the distance L between the reflectors should be an integral multiple of the half wavelength in the laser material. The latter is λ/η, where η is the refractive index of the laser material at the wavelength concerned, so the resonance condition is that

$$L = q\frac{\lambda}{2\eta} \qquad (7.4)$$

where q is an integer. From this we can see that the separation in wave numbers, $\Delta\left(\dfrac{1}{\lambda}\right)$, between consecutive axial mode resonances is

$$\Delta\left(\frac{1}{\lambda}\right) = q\frac{1}{2L\eta} \qquad (7.5)$$

In ruby at $0.69\ \mu$, the wavelength of the laser transition, the refractive index is 1.76 and the separation between modes is only 0.028 cm^{-1} for a rod 10 cm long. The value of the integer

q is of the order of 5×10^5. A more general equation for resonance, applicable to cylindrical specimens, is

$$\left(\frac{J_{nm}}{r}\right)^2 + \left(\frac{\pi q}{L}\right)^2 = k_1^2 \qquad (7.6)$$

where r is the specimen radius, J_{nm} is the mth root of the Bessel function of order n and

$$k_1^2 = \frac{4\pi^2\eta^2}{\lambda^2} \qquad (7.7)$$

The axial modes are given by $J_{00} = 0$ and the non-axial mode, the J_{01} mode, by $J_{01} = 2 \cdot 405$, and so on. From equation (7.6) the separations between the axial and non-axial modes are also found to be very small.

We must turn now to the question of diffraction losses in optical resonators. If we consider plane circular mirrors of radius a spaced a distance L apart, the field in the central region of the second mirror can be found by geometrical optics in terms of the field at the first mirror provided that $L \ll a^2/\lambda$ where as before λ is the free space wavelength. If $L > a^2/\lambda$ Fresnel zones are formed and diffraction losses occur. The parameter N, defined as

$$N = \frac{a^2}{\lambda L} \qquad (7.8)$$

gives a measure of the diffraction losses. For $N > 50$ losses are small and calculations based on geometrical optics are adequate. In practice lasers may have N values on both sides of this limit. Thus a ruby laser 7 cm long and 1 cm in diameter has an N value of about 900 at $0 \cdot 69 \ \mu$ so diffraction losses are negligible. On the other hand, a gas laser 100 cm long and $1 \cdot 5$ cm in diameter gives $N = 49$ at $\lambda = 1 \cdot 15 \ \mu$, and there is therefore a need to be able to assess diffraction losses for small values of N. Calculations of these have been made by Fox and Li (7.12) for

K

plane circular reflectors. The loss for the dominant axial and first non-axial modes is shown as a function of the value of N in Fig. 7.11 which illustrates the point that the non-axial modes

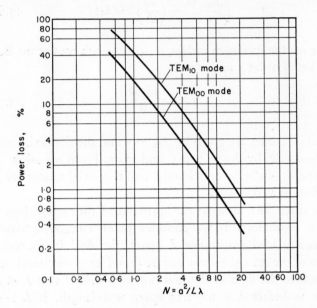

FIG. 7.11 Variation of the diffraction loss per transit with the parameter N for plane circular mirrors

suffer greater attenuation than the axial modes. Corresponding calculations were made for the confocal system by Boyd and Gordon (7.13) and in Table 7.1 the diffraction losses at small

Table 7.1

$N = \dfrac{a^2}{\lambda L}$	1	2	4
Loss: plane	0·18	0·08	0·03
spherical	11×10^{-5}	11×10^{-10}	11×10^{-20}

Diffraction losses with plane and spherical reflectors for small values of N

N values for the plane and spherical systems are compared. In this range the confocal system has a very much smaller loss. It is also less critical in alignment than the plane reflector system though the latter is convenient practically for solid laser materials because of the simplicity of the resulting structure.

References

7.1   MAIMAN, T. H.: *Nature*, 1960, **187**, p. 493.

7.2   ABELLA, I. D. and CUMMINS, H. Z.: *J. Appl. Phys.*, 1961, **32**, p. 1177.

7.3   SOROKIN, P. P. and STEVENSON, M. J.: *Phys. Rev. Lett.*, 1960, **5**, p. 557.

7.4   CARLSON, E. H. and DIEKE, G. H.: *J. Chem. Phys.*, 1961, **34**, p. 1602.

7.5   SNITZER, E.: *Phys. Rev. Lett.*, 1961, **7**, p. 444.

7.6   SCHAWLOW, A. L. and TOWNES, C. H.: *Phys. Rev.*, 1958, **112**, p. 1940.

7.7   JACOBS, S., GOULD, G. and RABINOWITZ, P.: *Phys. Rev. Lett.*, 1961, **7**, p. 415.

7.8   BASOV, N. G. and KROKHIN, O. N.: *Appl. Optics*, 1962, **1**, p. 213.

7.9   LENGYEL, B. A.: *Lasers* (Wiley, 1962).

7.10   JAVAN, A., BENNETT, W. R. and HERRIOTT, D. R.: *Phys. Rev. Lett.*, 1961, **6**, p. 106.

7.11   BENNETT, W. R.: *Appl. Opt. Supplement (Chemical Lasers)*, 1962, **1**, p. 24.

7.12   FOX, A. G. and LI, T.: *Bell Syst. Tech. J.*, 1961, **40**, p. 453.

7.13   BOYD, G. D. and GORDON, J. P.: *Bell Syst. Tech. J.*, 1961, **40**, p. 489.

8

Solid State Lasers

IN this Chapter the term *solid state* will be used to cover solid laser single crystals excluding semiconductors which will be considered as a separate class subsequently. There have been a great number of lasers reported since Maiman first obtained stimulated emission at 0·69 μ from a ruby crystal in 1960 and, rather than attempting to describe them all, the Chapter is confined simply to illustrating how the ideas of inversion outlined in Chapter 7 may be converted into operational devices. We shall see that in lasers as with masers a combination of techniques is required and that, although great developments have been made in a very short time, there are both fundamental and technological problems still to be solved. The first example to be described is the ruby laser because this demonstrates many of the features common to a number of solid state lasers.

8.1 The ruby laser

The first solid state laser (Maiman, 8.1) used ruby as the active material and emitted coherent light in a narrow band in the red part of the visible spectrum at 6943 Å. The experimental arrangement is indicated by Fig. 8.1 (similar systems have been used extensively by other workers). The ruby, containing 0·05% chromium, was in the form of a single crystal rod of about 1 cm diameter and length 10 cm. The polished plane end faces of the ruby rod were parallel to within 1 minute of arc. One end was silvered to give a completely reflecting surface and the other to give a partially reflecting surface with

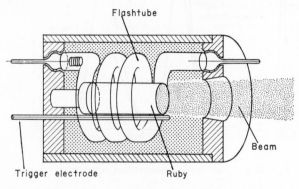

FIG. 8.1   Maiman's arrangement for pulsed excitation of ruby

about 10% transmission. Pumping energy was obtained from a spiral flash tube surrounding the ruby rod. This was xenon filled at about 125 mm Hg pressure and gave an output over a fairly wide spectral band in the green and blue, corresponding to the absorption bands in ruby, Fig. 8.2. The flash tube was actuated by discharging a condenser bank connected across it, and by using a capacity of about 100 microfarads at voltages of a few kilovolts input energies of up to 2000 joules could be obtained for periods of a few milliseconds. With input energies above a certain threshold value a beam of coherent radiation emerged from the partially silvered face of the ruby after each activation of the flash tube. The wavelength of this beam was found to be 6943 Å, corresponding to the laser transition shown in Fig. 7.2.

In later designs of ruby lasers efforts have been made to

increase the pumping efficiency which was rather low in the early experiments. For this purpose a reflecting cylinder of magnesium oxide surrounding the spiral flash tube was used by

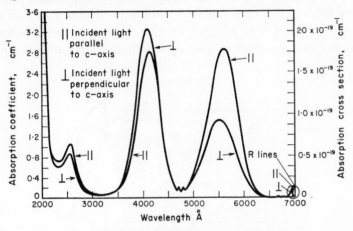

FIG. 8.2   The optical absorption spectrum of ruby

Collins et al. (8.2). The alternative arrangement of a linear flash tube placed at one focus of an elliptical reflector with the laser rod at the other focus has been widely employed, Fig. 8.3.

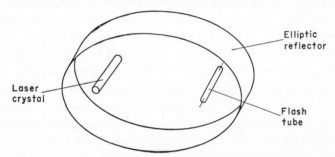

FIG. 8.3   Location of laser crystal and flash tube in an elliptic cylinder illuminator

Several designs of flash tube are available. These usually consist essentially of a quartz tube filled, for example, with xenon at low pressure and provided with electrodes between which the

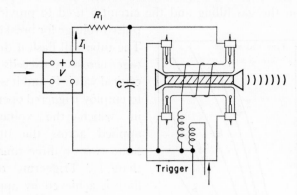

(*a*) Circuit arrangements, showing external triggering wire

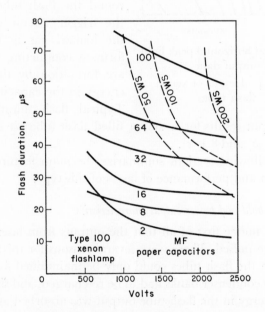

(*b*) Typical flash duration data (peak values)

FIG. 8.4   Details of xenon flash tubes

discharge occurs. The performance of a flash tube depends both on the gas filling and the circuitry used to provide the pulsed voltage for breakdown. The tube will flash if the voltage across it exceeds some critical value V_c and it is usual to employ triggered operation in which the voltage V applied across the tube is some two or three times less than V_c. Triggering of the flash is achieved by applying a sudden high voltage to an external trigger wire wrapped round the flash tube. When the trigger circuit operates, the ionized gas in the tube forms a conducting path for arc formation by the stored energy in the capacitor bank. Typical flash duration and light output results for a xenon filled flash tube are shown in Figs. 8.4 (b) and 8.4 (c).

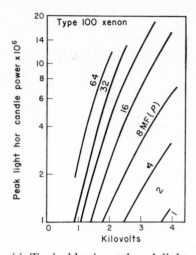

(c) Typical horizontal peak light output data

FIG. 8.4 Details of xenon flash tubes

The following sections summarize the main features of the operation and performance of lasers of this type.

(a) Threshold and power output characteristics

We may notice first of all that the outputs from lasers of this kind were pulsed. There were several reasons for this: the discharge in the flash tubes could only be maintained for a short time, the condenser banks had to be re-charged, and since most of the energy in the flash tube output was absorbed as heat by the ruby the crystal might have overheated and cracked.

When a low energy pulse was applied from the flash tube (less than 1000 joules in Collins' experiments) fluorescent radiation from the R_1 and R_2 levels was observed. Fluorescence began immediately the flash tube was actuated and this radiation emerged from the ruby in all directions. By examining that fraction escaping through the partially silvered end the intensity ratio of the R_1 and R_2 radiation was found to be nearly unity. When the flash tube energy exceeded a certain threshold value (about 2000 joules in Collins' equipment) the character of the emitted radiation changed and a well-defined beam emerged in which the intensity ratio R_1/R_2 had been increased by several thousand times. The fluorescent radiation obtained below threshold represented spontaneous emission and the R_1 radiation emitted in the well collimated beam above threshold was stimulated emission. The occurrence of a threshold energy corresponds to the condition that the overall gain in the laser rod must exceed all losses in order for there to be a net gain resulting in oscillation. Its value is a function of the laser geometry, the spectral content of the flash tube output, the optical constants of the laser material and the transition probabilities for the energy levels utilized. Because of this the threshold energy for a given material and system is temperature dependent and, as we can see from Table 8.1, it is advantageous

Table 8.1

Temperature (°C)	Threshold power (Watts cm^{-3})
20	550
100	1100
150	1800
200	3000

The temperature variation of threshold pump power for a ruby laser

to keep the laser crystal as cool as possible. Above the threshold the optical output increases with the input energy until the material is saturated. At first the dependence is linear, as shown by Fig. 8.5 which is taken from results obtained by Koozekanani et al. (8.3).

The stimulated emission does not begin until a short time after the application of the flash tube pulse. With flash tube pulses a few milliseconds long at energies just above threshold

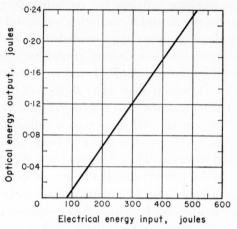

FIG. 8.5   The optical output versus electrical input characteristic for a pulsed ruby laser

the delay was typically 0·5 ms and corresponds to the time taken for the amplification to build up to oscillation conditions. The emitted R_1 radiation was found to consist of a number of

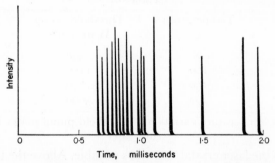

FIG. 8.6   Spiking in the output from a pulsed ruby laser

narrow spikes, Fig. 8.6, each of which was of about 1 μs duration. The reason for this relaxation oscillation effect is that during oscillation the population of the upper level is reduced more rapidly than it is being increased by the excitation process. Thus the population difference across the laser transition falls below the critical value for maintaining oscillation which therefore ceases until the original conditions are re-established.

Because of the spiky nature of the laser output we must distinguish between the total energy radiated during one excitation and the energy contained in a single narrow spike. The former, the mean output energy, is typically between about 0·1 and 1·5 joule and depends on the excitation efficiency, the quality of the ruby crystal and the alignment of the reflectors. The latter, representing the peak power obtainable in a single pulse of coherent radiation, can be very high because the pulse width is so small and values exceeding several tens of kilowatts have been reported. This ability to give extremely high power outputs is one of the major features of solid state lasers and we shall return to this point later.

(b) Coherency, beam width and spectral width

The coherency of the emitted beam of stimulated radiation may be examined in several ways. Indirect evidence comes from the observation, mentioned in the preceding section, that above threshold the emitted radiation forms a narrow beam emerging from the partially silvered reflector. Direct studies of coherency have been made by leaving small rectangular apertures in the silvering at one end of the laser rod and comparing the Fraunhofer diffraction pattern obtained with that predicted for coherent radiation. In this way it was found that for distances of the order of a hundred wavelengths across an end surface the emitted radiation corresponded to coherent plane illumination of the aperture. Examination of the emitted light intensity across the end face showed that isolated luminous spots are first observed. Just above threshold the individual spots may be about 100 μ in diameter and clusters of dimensions up to 850 μ are formed at higher input levels (Evtuhov and Neeland, 8.4). This effect is thought to be related to the crystalline quality of the ruby, emission being obtained initially from axial filaments of uniform refractive index. The polarization properties of the stimulated radiation depend on the crystallographic orientation of the ruby. If the rod is cut so that its longitudinal axis coincides with the crystallographic c-axis the radiation is unpolarized. If, however, the rod axis makes an angle of 60° or 90° to the c-axis the radiation is plane polarized in a plane perpendicular to the c-axis which, in ruby, is also the optic axis. (The angles of 60° and 90° arise as a result of the methods used in growing synthetic ruby crystals. This is discussed in detail in Chapter 12.)

The value of the angular width of the laser beam is calculable from diffraction theory. We require to know the width from the centre of a principal maximum to the first zero, θ_0, for the multiple beam interferometer formed by the reflectors. Assuming uniform amplitude over the reflectors this is

$$\theta_0 = 1 \cdot 22 \frac{\lambda}{d} \qquad (8.1)$$

where d is the reflector diameter which is usually the same as that of the laser rod. For a ruby rod 1 cm in diameter this leads to a predicted beam width of only about 16 seconds of arc. This is considerably smaller than many of the experimental beam widths reported, most of which lie between about 0·3° and 1°. The difference is again thought to be due to crystalline imperfections and we may notice that the observed beam widths correspond more nearly to the predicted values for reflectors of the size of the individual spots observed in the optical output.

It is rather difficult to define the meaning of the spectral width of the stimulated radiation from a ruby laser because, as we have seen, the axial cavity modes are so closely spaced that usually several are excited. Discussion of this topic will therefore be deferred until gas lasers, which may be made to operate in a single mode, have been described. We may note, however, that the width of the fluorescent line observed under non-stimulated conditions is 3 Å whereas under laser oscillation conditions spectral line widths of less than 5×10^{-4} Å have been reported. The narrowing arises because the emission is generated in a high Q cavity, as in the ammonia maser.

8.2 Other single crystal lasers

A number of other single crystal materials have been used for lasers, in particular the fluorides, tungstates and molybdates

Table 8.2

Host lattice	Doping ion	Concentration (mole per cent)	Emission wavelength (μ)
Al_2O_3	Cr^{3+}	0·01–0·05	0·6943
Al_2O_3	Cr^{3+}	0·3–0·5	0·701
CaF_2	U^{3+}	0·05	2·24, 2·49, 2·613 17
CaF_2	Sm^{2+}	0·05	0·708
CaF_2	Dy^{2+}	0·03	2·36
CaF_2	Tm^{2+}	0·05	1·116, 1·189
CaF_2	Nd^{3+}	u*	1·046
BaF_2	U^{3+}	u*	2·556
SrF_2	U^{3+}	0·1	2·407
SrF_2	Sm^{2+}	u*	0·696
$CaWO_4$	Nd^{3+}	0·14	1·063 – 1·065
$CaWO_4$	Ho^{3+}	0·5	2·046
$CaWO_4$	Tm^{3+}	0·5	1·911
$CaWO_4$	Pr^{3+}	0·05	1·406
$CaWO_4$	Er^{3+}	u*	1·612
$SrMoO_4$	Nd^{3+}	u*	1·064
$SrMoO_4$	Pr^{3+}	0·05	1·047

Emission wavelengths for some doped single crystal laser materials

* Concentration unknown

doped with rare earth ions. These materials are somewhat easier to grow in high quality single crystal form than ruby as they have lower melting points and so different growth techniques can be applied. The laser emission wavelengths for some of these materials are given in Table 8.2. Comparatively few of them share with ruby the ability to operate at room temperature.

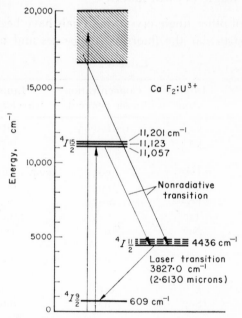

FIG. 8.7   Energy levels of U^{3+} in CaF_2

The uranium laser (Sorokin and Stevenson, 8.5, Boyd et al. 8.6) introduces some new features of which perhaps the most marked is that the low threshold energies required enable continuous operation to be achieved. The energy level diagram of U^{3+} in CaF_2 is shown again in Fig. 8.7. (The uranium ion may occupy sites of either tetragonal or trigonal symmetry. Fig. 8.7 applies to the case of a uranium concentration of 0·05 molar per cent distributed evenly between the two kinds of site.) The laser transition is between the lowest $^4I_{11/2}$ level and the $^4I_{9/2}$ level lying 609 cm^{-1} above the ground state and occurs at a wavelength of 2·61 μ. The experimental arrangement used by Boyd et al. is shown in Fig. 8.8. This enabled a variety of

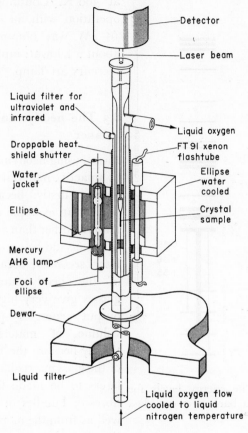

FIG. 8.8 Experimental arrangement for the cw uranium laser

sources to be used for optical pumping and also allowed low temperature operation to be studied. It was found that the major part of the excitation of the laser transition was by absorption from the ground state to the $^4I_{15/2}$ levels. The threshold energy was found to be very dependent on the crystal temperature and rose from 3·0 joules at 77°K to about 1200 joules at 300°K corresponding to a reduction in the lifetime of the metastable $^4I_{11/2}$ state from 130 μs at 77°K to less than 15 μs at 300°K. Continuous laser operation with an output of 10 μW was obtained using about a kilowatt input from a mercury arc lamp.

8.3 The neodymium glass laser

Lasers using neodymium glass as an active material are noteworthy, firstly, because they present an example of a solid material other than a synthetic single crystal being used for a laser, secondly, because some of the neodymium doped glasses give very high optical output energies per unit volume of material, and thirdly because the versatility of the glass matrix has enabled

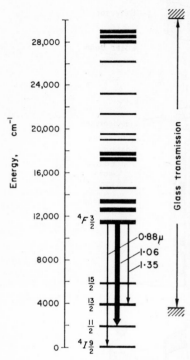

FIG. 8.9 The energy levels for Nd³⁺ in a barium crown-glass base

lasers to be made from thin fibres or bundles of fibres as well as from the more conventional rods.

The energy level scheme for Nd³⁺ in barium crown glass is shown in Fig. 8.9 (Snitzer, 8.7). The $^4F_{3/2}$ level is fluorescent and the laser transitions are from this to the $^4I_{13/2}$, $^4I_{11/2}$ and $^4I_{9/2}$ states at wavelengths of 0·88 μ, 1·06 μ and 1·35 μ respectively. Excitation is accomplished by optical pumping from the ground state to levels above the $^4F_{3/2}$ state. About a third is provided by absorption to the three levels in the infra-red, a further third by the strong absorptions in the yellow region at about 17 000 cm^{-1} and the remainder by the other levels, particularly the ultra-violet absorptions near 28 000 cm^{-1}. The

nature of the $^4I_{9/2}$ ground state depends on the chemical composition of the glass matrix. With high lead content silica glasses and with lanthanum borate glasses it appears as a singlet, but in alkali–alkali–earth silicate glasses the ground state is split into two levels separated by energies of about 400 cm^{-1}. This splitting of the ground state implies that all the strong absorptions have additional bands on the long wavelength side, Fig. 8.10, which are observable at room temperature but not at low temperatures. The result of this is that neodymium glass lasers are most efficiently pumped at room temperature. The lifetime of the fluorescent radiation from the $^4F_{3/2}$ state also varies considerably

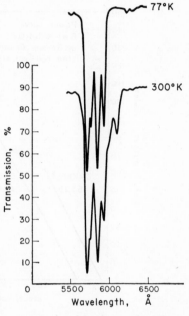

FIG. 8.10 The absorption spectra of Nd^{3+} in barium crown glass at 300°K and 77°K; the curve for 77°K is displaced vertically to avoid overlapping traces

with the chemistry of the glass and in barium crown glass has at 0·75 ms one of the longest observed values.

In one of Snitzer's experiments a concentration of 6% neodymium was used in a laser rod consisting of an inner core of doped crown glass 6 mm diameter and 45 cm long, coated, except at its ends, with a layer of undoped glass of lower refractive index to give total internal reflection. A 45 cm long xenon flash tube was used for pumping in a close coupling configuration. It was placed alongside the laser rod and the flash tube and rod were together wrapped in silver foil which served as a reflector. With the arrangement average optical

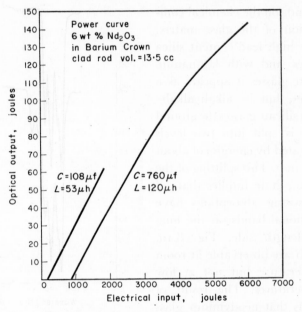

FIG. 8.11   Neodymium laser characteristic for optical output versus electrical input to the xenon flash tube

outputs of up to 140 joules were obtained in pulses of overall duration of about a millisecond. The input–output characteristic is shown in Fig. 8.11 in which the departure from linearity was due to overloading of the flash tube. Above threshold the conversion efficiency was 3·9% and the energy output per unit volume of laser material was rather greater than 10 joules per cc.

In configurations giving narrow beam widths characteristic random spiking of the laser output was observed with both coated and uncoated rods. With coated rods limit cycle behaviour was also observed in which only a few output oscillations were obtained. In these circumstances energies of as much as half a joule were concentrated in a single spike, corresponding to peak powers of a megawatt.

The wavelength range over which laser emission occurred varied with the input pump power, Fig. 8.12, and increased to

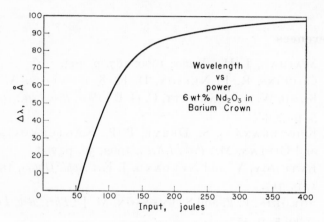

FIG. 8.12 The variation of the spectral width of laser emission, $\Delta\lambda$, with power for a neodymium laser

an approximately constant value of 100 Å at the highest power levels. However, by using a pinhole and lens arrangement to provide strong mode selection (cf. Skinner and Geusic, 8.8) Snitzer showed that the same laser output intensity pattern was obtained from both reflecting ends which indicated that the neodymium glass rod was of such high optical quality that the field distribution of the single mode selected by the pinhole arrangement was not distorted. In this instance the laser output was confined within a beam width of about 20 seconds of arc.

Laser emission has also been obtained from neodymium crown glass fibres. With 8 μ diameter fibres 1 metre long laser output pulses as short as 0·1 μs were obtained. A rod composed of a bundle of fibres may also be used. In this arrangement each fibre acts as an independent laser and the threshold energy for this kind of assemblage was shown to be only between one-tenth and one-third of that which would have been required for a solid rod of the same total diameter. The fibre assembly is also useful for estimating the pump power distribution across a rod by measuring the laser output intensities of individual fibres in different positions in the rod.

References

8.1   MAIMAN, T. H.: *Nature*, 1960, **187**, p. 493.

8.2   COLLINS, R. J., NELSON, D. F., SCHAWLOW, A. L., BOND, W. and GARRETT, C. G. B.: *Phys. Rev. Lett.*, 1960, **5**, p. 303.

8.3   KOOZEKANANI, S., DEBYE, P. P., KRUTCHKOFF, A. and CIFTAN, M.: *Proc. I.R.E.*, 1962, **50**, p. 207.

8.4   EVTUHOV, V. and NEELAND, J. K.: *Appl. Optics*, 1962, **1**, p. 517.

8.5   SOROKIN, P. P. and STEVENSON, M. J.: *Phys. Rev. Lett.*, 1960, **5**, p. 557.

8.6   BOYD, G. D., COLLINS, R. J., PORTO, S. P. S., YARIV, A. and HARGREAVES, W. A.: *Phys. Rev. Lett.*, 1962, **8**, p. 269.

8.7   SNITZER, E.: *Phys. Rev. Lett.*, 1961, **7**, p. 444.

8.8   SKINNER, J. G. and GEUSIC, J. E.: *J. Opt. Soc. Am.*, 1962, **52**, p. 1319.

9

Gas Lasers

ONE of the first gas lasers was constructed in 1960 by Javan, Bennett and Herriott (9.1) using a helium–neon mixture as the active material. Since then so large a number of suitable energy level systems have been found in a variety of gases that Bennett (9.2), in a review article in 1965, was able to include a list of nearly five hundred observed laser transitions. The wavelength range covered by these extends from the ultra-violet through the visible and infra-red to the submillimetre region of the spectrum. As it is not possible to describe all these advances within the space of a single Chapter attention will be confined to discussion of some of the experimental techniques involved in the operation of gas lasers and of performance characteristics, taking only a few of the many lasers which have been reported as examples illustrating the more general features.

9.1 Helium–neon lasers

The form of Javan, Bennett and Herriott's early helium–neon laser is shown in Fig. 9.1. It was basically a discharge tube with plane reflectors mounted internally at the ends. The system was filled with a mixture of helium and neon at pressures of 1·0 and

0·1 mm Hg respectively. The reflectors, which were flat to a hundredth of a wavelength, were supported on special mounts which enabled them to be aligned for parallelism to within 6

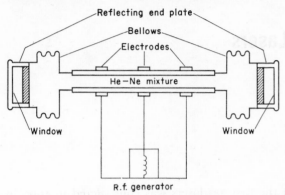

FIG. 9.1   Schematic diagram of Javan, Bennett and Herriott's helium–neon laser

seconds of arc. Multiple dielectric layer coatings (9.3) were used in forming the reflectors whose reflectance and transmittance characteristics are given in Fig. 9.2. Near the operating

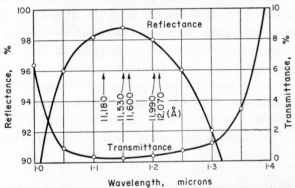

FIG. 9.2   The reflectance and transmittance characteristics for the reflectors used in Javan, Bennett and Herriott's laser

wavelength of 1·15 μ the reflectivity was 98·9%. The discharge in the helium–neon mixture was excited with a 30 Mc/s supply connected to electrodes spaced along the tube. The spacing between the reflectors was about 100 cm and the discharge tube had a bore of 1·5 cm. Continuous oscillations were obtained at wavelengths of 1·118, 1·153, 1·160, 1·119 and 1·207 μ, the strongest line being at 1·153 μ. The power outputs at these wavelengths were between 1 mW and 4 mW.

One of the disadvantages of this form of construction is the complication of the bellows necessary for the internal manipulation of the reflectors. An alternative system is to use spherical reflectors placed external to the discharge tube, Fig. 9.3. When

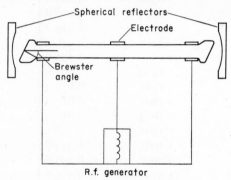

FIG. 9.3   Arrangement of a helium–neon laser using external confocal spherical reflectors

external reflectors are used in this way it is necessary to minimize unwanted reflections from the windows at the ends of the discharge tube. This is achieved by orienting the windows at the Brewster angle for the plane polarized component required. With confocal systems of this type the need for precision adjustments inside the vacuum is avoided. The accuracy of alignment required with the confocal system is also much less than with plane reflectors. Further studies of the emission lines obtained from helium–neon have been made with confocal systems using discharge tubes up to 10 metres long filled at various gas pressures. Some of the laser transitions observed with helium–neon mixtures are given in Table 9.1. Altogether over one hundred and fifty laser transitions in the neon spectrum have been observed, distributed fairly evenly over a range of wavelengths from 0·33 μ to 124·6 μ. Further details are given in Reference 9.2.

Table 9.1

Transition (Paschen)	Wavelength (μm)	Wave no. (cm^{-1})	Pressure (mm Hg) (He/Ne)
$3s_2$–$2p_4$	0·6328	15 802·8	0·4/0·1
$2s_3$–$2p_7$	1·0798	9 261·0	
$2s_2$–$2p_6$	1·0845	9 220·8	
$2s_4$–$2p_8$	1·1143	8 974·2	1–2/0·1–0·2
$2s_5$–$2p_9$	1·1177	8 946·9	
$2s_5$–$2p_8$	1·1390	8 779·6	
$2s_2$–$2p_5$	1·1409	8 765·0	
$2s_2$–$2p_4$	1·1523	8 678·3	1/0·1
$2s_2$–$2p_3$	1·1601	8 619·9	
$2s_3$–$2p_5$	1·1614	8 610·3	
$2s_2$–$2p_2$	1·1767	8 498·3	
$2s_3$–$2p_2$	1·1985	8 343·8	1–2/0·1–0·2
$2s_5$–$2p_6$	1·2066	8 287·8	
$2s_2$–$2p_1$	1·5231	6 565·6	

Some laser transitions in the helium–neon system

The beam width, measured to half power points, in the original plane reflector laser was 1 minute of arc when the reflectors were set exactly parallel. With external confocal mirrors the beam is less well defined and has a width of some 30 minutes. This may be reduced by placing a limiting aperture in front of the exit mirror. The beam width θ_L obtained with a circular limiting aperture and a spacing L between the reflectors is given by

$$\theta_L = 0.93 \left(\frac{\lambda}{L}\right)^{\frac{1}{2}} \qquad (9.1)$$

where λ is the wavelength of the radiation and θ_L is measured in radians (Boyd and Gordon, 9.4). In this way beam widths of about 3 minutes of arc have been obtained in confocal systems.

Just as in solid state lasers the cavity modes in the gas laser are very closely spaced in wavelength. Although the Brewster angle windows at the ends of the discharge tube are, strictly speaking, suitable for the passage of only one plane polarized component, other polarizations are supported when the input power level is raised well above threshold and so several cavity modes may be simultaneously excited. Oscillations may therefore occur at all the cavity resonances which fall within the linewidth of the atomic resonance. The situation is depicted in Fig. 9.4. The natural linewidth of the neon $1 \cdot 152 \, \mu$ transition is

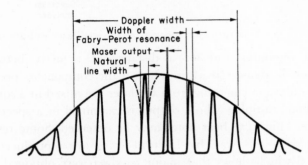

FIG. 9.4   The relationship between the cavity, Doppler and laser emission linewidths in a helium–neon laser

of the order of 90 Mc/s, but in the discharge the linewidth is increased by an order of magnitude by Doppler broadening to about 900 Mc/s. Because the laser radiation is generated in a high Q resonator the oscillation linewidth $\Delta\omega_0$ is narrower than the normal linewidth $\Delta\omega$ by an amount which depends on the power level P of the oscillations in the resonator. For oscillation in a single mode, assuming that the linewidth is governed by spontaneous emission into that mode, the value of $\Delta\omega_0$ is given by

$$\Delta\omega_0 = \frac{2\hbar\omega}{P} (\Delta\omega)^2 \qquad (9.2)$$

where ω is the angular frequency of the radiation. For a continuous laser output of 5 mW the linewidth predicted by equation (9.2) for wavelengths near $1\cdot15$ μ is only about 7×10^{-4} c/s. Thus we see that in a gas laser oscillations may occur simultaneously in several modes, the spectral width of each frequency component being very narrow.

The separation of the simultaneous modes of oscillation depends, as we have seen in Section 7.4, on the length of the

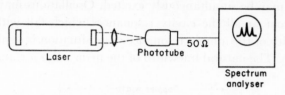

Laser Phototube 50 Ω Spectrum analyser

FIG. 9.5 Apparatus for spectral analysis of laser radiation

optical resonator and for a distance of 1 metre between reflectors is about 150 Mc/s. Thus, if the components present in the radiation emerging from the laser are mixed in a square law photomultiplier whose output is examined in a spectrum analyser (Fig. 9.5) beat notes may be observed. Some results obtained in this way by Herriott (9.5) are reproduced in Fig. 9.6 which shows that major maxima were obtained 148

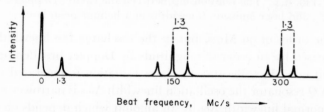

Beat frequency, Mc/s ⟶

FIG. 9.6 Beat notes produced by a helium–neon laser

Mc/s apart, corresponding to axial modes for the 1 metre reflector spacing used. There was also a non-axial mode present in the laser output which gave satellite lines $1\cdot3$ Mc/s away from the major maxima.

Observation of the beat frequencies forms a method for estimating the spectral width of the laser emission, which, because it is some 10^7 times smaller than the sharpest line obtainable from conventional optical sources, cannot be measured by standard optical techniques. Two difficulties arise, however. In the first place since the resonant frequency for a given cavity mode depends directly on the reflector spacing very small changes in this due to temperature fluctuations or microphony cause frequency changes at least as large as the linewidth. Secondly, frequency pulling occurs between the interferometer and atomic resonances, and each interferometer mode is shifted towards the centre frequency of the atomic resonance line. If the reflector spacing is adjusted to bring one of the cavity resonances exactly into coincidence with the centre of the atomic emission line oscillation will occur at this centre frequency. As we have seen the width of the cavity mode $\Delta\omega_c$ is normally very much less than the Doppler width of the atomic emission line $\Delta\omega_D$ and in these circumstances the oscillation frequency ω_0 of an adjacent mode is given by

$$\omega_0 = \omega_c + (\omega_D - \omega_c) \frac{\Delta\omega_c}{\Delta\omega_D} \qquad (9.3)$$

in which ω_c and ω_D are the centre frequencies of the cavity resonance and the Doppler broadened atomic line respectively. This equation shows that the shift due to frequency pulling depends on the deviation of the cavity mode from the centre of the atomic resonance and so any change in the length of the interferometer affects different modes in different ways. There will be a corresponding effect on the beat frequency unless modes of oscillation are selected for which the shifts due to frequency pulling are exactly compensated. Javan, Ballik and Bond (9.6) investigated the stability of a helium–neon laser by this method and found that a short-term stability in beat frequency of better than 2 c/s could be obtained. This indicated that the degree of monochromaticity in the laser beam was about 1 part in 10^{14}. In further experiments made to assess the stability characteristics of helium–neon lasers the outputs of two independent lasers were mixed in the same photomultiplier,

Fig. 9.7. Here it was not only necessary to expose the same region of the photocathode to the two incident laser beams but also to ensure by means of the autocollimator that their wave-fronts were parallel. With this system Javan, Ballik and Bond found a drift of only 2 parts in 10^9 in the beat frequency over periods of about a hundred seconds.

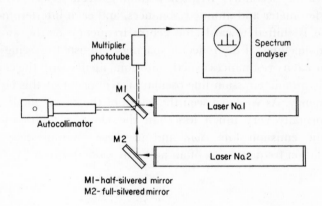

FIG. 9.7   Schematic diagram of arrangement for mixing the outputs of two gas lasers

✳ 9.2 Noble gas lasers

Stimulated emission at wavelengths between $2\ \mu$ and $28\ \mu$ has been obtained from gas lasers using pure noble gases (e.g. McFarlane, Faust, Patel and Garrett, 9.7). Population in-version can be maintained by electron collision with ground state atoms and resonant coincidence of excited levels of two different atomic species is not required. While the basic design of the gas lasers described so far may be retained some additional special features are required for operation at these longer wavelengths. These are illustrated by McFarlane's laser, shown diagrammatically in Fig. 9.8. In this confocal mirrors were used to facilitate alignment but they were placed inside the vacuum envelope. This avoided the use, within the optical cavity, of any lossy material necessary for making Brewster angle windows. In order to provide uniformly high reflectivity beyond 2 μ vacuum evaporated silver and aluminium mirrors were used and with these a wide range of wavelength could be explored without changing mirrors. One of the mirrors was

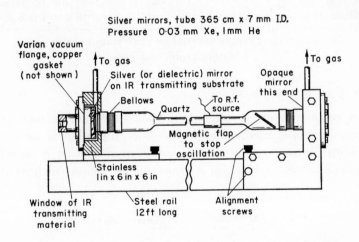

FIG. 9.8 Internal confocal mirror system used for studying noble gas lasers

partially transmitted and was deposited on a substrate such as silicon or germanium so as to transmit in the infra-red; the laser beam emerged through this mirror. The discharge tube length was 365 cm and bores of 15 mm and 7 mm were used. The discharge was excited by either a radio-frequency or 60 c/s a.c. voltage.

Stimulated emission in pure neon, argon, krypton and xenon was studied. The wavelength ranges covered by the emission lines in these gases are indicated by Table 9.2 which includes data obtained in various laser systems at different gas pressures.

Table 9.2

Gas	No. of laser emission lines observed	Wavelength range covered
Argon	85	0·2753 μ to 26·956 μ
Krypton	58	0·3239 μ to 7·0565 μ
Xenon	64	0·2983 μ to 18·500 μ
Neon, including Ne in He–Ne	155	0·2678 μ to 132·8 μ

The wavelength ranges covered by laser transitions in argon, krypton, xenon and neon

✱ 9.3 Cascade lasers

In cascade lasers a different method of obtaining inverted populations is used, namely, one laser transition is used to pump another in the same atomic species. This is shown schematically in Fig. 9.9. A conventional means (such as an

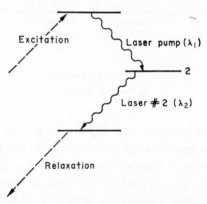

FIG. 9.9   The stages involved in stimulated emission pumping

r.f. discharge) is used to populate the highest level from the ground state. Stimulated emission at the wavelength λ_1 enhances the population of level 2 and so enables a second laser oscillation to occur between levels 2 and 1. The excess population in level 1 can be removed either by normal relaxation processes or by the stimulated emission from a third laser transition. We can see that in this technique the optical cavity must be simultaneously resonant at two oscillation wavelengths. In most of the experimental systems a single optical resonator was used and the gain at the pumping transition frequency was sufficient to compensate for non-optimum coatings on the reflectors. In some, however, either doubly resonant hybrid mirrors or broad band metallic reflectors were used.

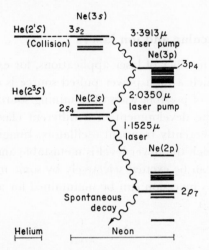

FIG. 9.10   The cascade sequence used to obtain the 1·1525 μ neon emission line in helium–neon

The laser pumping technique is particularly useful in populating levels of the same parity as the ground state which are difficult to excite by electron collision with ground state atoms. One example of this is in the excitation of the 1·1525 μ neon transition in a helium–neon mixture (Bennett and Knutson, 9.8). The cascade process is shown in Fig. 9.10. A gas discharge is used in the normal manner to produce excitation of the neon $^3S_2$ level by collision with helium atoms in the 2^1S state. The laser oscillation at 3·391 μ, a transition which has a high gain, populates the neon $^3p_4$ state to such an extent that a second laser oscillation is obtained at 2·035 μ. This in turn enhances the population in the neon $2s_4$ level and because an excess population can thus be established across the $2s_4$ and $2p_7$ levels a third laser oscillation at 1·1525 μ can be obtained.

This method is useful in allowing oscillation to occur between levels which are normally difficult to invert. Large numbers of four-sequence laser cascades have been reported by Patel and Kerl (9.9) in the molecular spectrum of carbon monoxide.

✳ 9.4 Molecular and ion lasers

There are a number of laser applications, for example optical radar, in which a high power pulsed source is desirable. The investigation of possible ways of obtaining sources of this kind has led to the development of a different class of gas lasers which are inherently transient oscillators. Imagine a two-level system in which the lower level is metastable and in which the upper level can be excited selectively by some means. In these circumstances inversion can be maintained for a short time Δt providing that

$$\Delta t \leqslant \frac{1}{2A_{21}}$$

where A_{21} is the Einstein A coefficient for the transition from the upper to the lower level (Bennett, 9.2). After time intervals longer than Δt the population in the lower state starts to exceed that in the upper state and so, even in the absence of additional relaxation processes, the transition will become absorbing. To obtain inversion the excitation pulse rise time and duration must be short compared to Δt and this is achieved by using a high energy pulsed discharge in the gas. One of the first gas lasers of this type was reported by Mathias and Parker (9.10), who used pure nitrogen at pressures of between 1 and 4 mm Hg in a long interferometer. Excitation was provided by passing a high current high voltage discharge through the gas and stimulated emission was obtained from some twenty-five transitions in the first positive bands of nitrogen. The wavelengths and relative intensities of these lines are shown in Table 9.3. Molecular transitions have also been observed in carbon

Table 9.3

Wavelength in air (μ)	Relative intensity	Wavelength in air (μ)	Relative intensity
2–1 Band		0–0 Band	
0·868 35	0·1	1·044 93	0·006
0·869 12	1	1·046 12	0·01
0·869 80	1	1·047 23	0·1
0·870 44	1	1·048 00	1
0·870 99	0·2	1·049 09	0·06
1–0 Band		1·049 48	0·4
0·884 40	0·005	1·050 52	0·08
0·884 78	0·04	0–1 Band	
0·885 23	0·03	1·230 3	0·01
0·885 63	0·07	1·231 2	1
0·886 25	0·05	1·231 9	0·04
0·887 11	0·3	1·233 4	0·1
0·887 90	1	1·234 7	0·06
0·888 65	1		
0·889 27	1		
0·889 89	0·4		
0·890 93	0·06		

Laser transitions obtained in the first positive band of nitrogen

monoxide (9.11), carbon dioxide (9.12), deuterium oxide (9.13) and water vapour (9.14). In the studies on water vapour laser cavities 5 metres long were used with discharge tubes of diameter ranging from 2·5 cm to 5 cm. Oscillation was observed during high current high voltage pulsed discharges through vapour at 1 mm Hg pressure. The wavelengths of the emission lines and the peak powers obtained are given in Table 9.4. We may notice especially the power level of 7 watts peak obtainable from the line at 33·03 μ. An aluminized silicon mirror was used for the output coupling at these wavelengths.

Table 9.4

Vacuum wavelength (μ)	Peak power (W)	Vacuum wavelength (μ)	Peak power (W)
16·931	0·02	45·523	0·007
23·365	0·1	47·251	0·08
26·666	0·5	47·469	0·06
27·974	3	47·693	0·04
28·054	—	48·677	0·07
28·273	0·6	53·906	0·000 8
28·356	0·01	55·077	0·06
32·929	0·4	57·660	0·02
33·033	7	67·177	0·01
35·000	—	73·402	0·002
35·841	0·1	78·455	0·007
36·619	0·009	79·106	0·006
37·859	0·003	89·775	0·006
38·094	—	115·42	0·000 7
39·698	0·1	118·65	0·001
40·629	0·01	120·08	—

Laser transitions observed in water vapour

Pulsed laser operation has also been observed between excited ionic states in a number of gases. Transitions of this type were initially seen in the visible spectrum of mercury (Hg II) by Bell (9.15). Similar effects were subsequently found in ionized argon, neon, krypton and xenon (9.16) and in singly and multiply ionized oxygen, carbon, nitrogen and chlorine (9.17). In the pulsed discharges used in these experiments current densities of hundreds of amperes per square centimetre and fields of several kilovolts per centimetre are produced and plasma interactions, notably the pinch effect, may dominate the excitation process. In argon at pressures between 0·01 and 0·04 mm Hg and at current densities of about 10^3 A/cm^2 very high gains, exceeding 10 db/m in 2 mm diameter discharge tubes, have been obtained for the emission line at 4765 Å and super-radiance has been observed on three transitions.

References

9.1 JAVAN, A., BENNETT, W. R. and HERRIOTT, D. R.: *Phys. Rev. Lett.*, 1961, **6**, p. 106.

9.2 BENNETT, W. R.: *Appl. Optics Supplement on Chemical Lasers*, 1965, p. 3.

9.3 HEAVENS, O. S.: *Optical Masers* (Methuen, 1964), p. 97.

9.4 BOYD, G. D. and GORDON, J. P.: *Bell Syst. Tech. J.*, 1961, **40**, p. 489.

9.5 HERRIOTT, D. R.: *J. Opt. Soc. Amer.*, 1962, **52**, p. 31.

9.6 JAVAN, A., BALLIK, E. A. and BOND, W. L.: *J. Opt. Soc. Amer.*, 1962, **52**, p. 96.

9.7 McFARLANE, R. A., FAUST, W. L., PATEL, G. K. N. and GARRETT, C. G. B.: *Quantum Electronics III* (Columbia University Press, 1964), p. 573.

9.8 BENNETT, W. R. and KNUTSON, J. W.: *Proc. I.E.E.E.* 1964, **52**, p. 864.

9.9 PATEL, G. K. N. and KERL, R. J.: *Appl. Phys. Lett.*, 1964, **5**, p. 81.

9.10 MATHIAS, L. E. S. and PARKER, J. T.: *Appl. Phys. Lett.*, 1963, **3**, p. 16.

9.11 MATHIAS, L. E. S. and PARKER, J. T.: *Phys. Lett.*, 1963, **7**, p. 194.

9.12 PATEL, G. K. N.: *Phys. Rev. Lett.*, 1964, **12**, p. 588 and **13**, p. 617.

9.13 GEBBIE, H. A., STONE, N. W. B., FINDLEY, F. D. and ROBB, J. A.: *Nature*, 1964, **202**, p. 169.

9.14 CROCKER, A., GEBBIE, H. A., KIMMITT, M. F. and MATHIAS, L. E. S.: *Nature*, 1964, **201**, p. 250.

9.15 BELL, W. E.: *Appl. Phys. Lett.*, 1964, **4**, p. 34.

9.16 BRIDGES, W. B.: *Appl. Phys. Lett.*, 1964, **4**, p. 128.

9.17 McFARLANE, R. A.: *Appl. Phys. Lett.*, 1964, **5**, p. 91.

10

Semiconductor and Liquid Lasers

IN addition to the solid state and gaseous laser systems described in the preceding two Chapters laser action has been observed in two other distinct classes of material. These are, firstly, in some semiconductors, notably gallium arsenide and lead selenide, and secondly, in a few liquids particularly solutions of the rare earth chelates. This Chapter summarizes the main features of these lasers. In both types the basic principle of obtaining laser action by establishing a favourable population difference across the laser transition is retained although widely different methods are used to achieve inversion.

10.1 Semiconductor lasers

As described in Section 7.3 radiation is produced in many semiconducting materials when electrons and holes recombine and it is this process which, under the correct conditions, can be used to generate coherent radiation. The recombination energy can, however, be dissipated in a number of other ways which are non-radiative, for example by direct interaction with lattice phonons other holes or free electrons or by exchange processes with impurity levels. In many semiconductors these non-radiative processes predominate so that the probability of radiative recombination occurring is small. However, in some semiconductors, e.g. in gallium arsenide, the transition probability for radiative decay of an electron-hole pair is high and, since it is also possible to achieve adequate population inversions, laser action can be obtained. In these materials the maximum energy of the valence band and the minimum energy of the conduction band both occur at the same point in K-space (at $K = 0$ for gallium arsenide), and a radiative transition is allowed because the wave functions of the two states are of opposite parity. The wavelength of the recombination radiation is confined to a fairly narrow range corresponding to the band edge. Two of the novel features of semiconductor lasers are the method of pumping and the optical resonator. Population inversion is obtained by minority carrier injection across a forward biased p–n junction. The optical resonator is formed round the junction by the material itself and this feature leads to devices of very small dimensions.

(a) Gallium arsenide diode lasers

Semiconductor diode laser action was first obtained in gallium arsenide. (For a review of III–V compound lasers see, for example, Burns and Nathan, 10.1.) One form of construction used by Kingsley and Fenner (10.2) is shown in Fig. 10.1 which

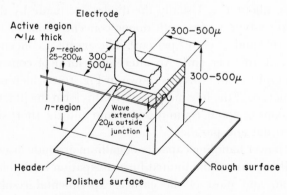

FIG. 10.1   Schematic diagram of a gallium arsenide
laser diode

also indicates the small size of the unit. Two opposite surfaces which are perpendicular to the plane of the junction are polished flat and parallel to within a few wavelengths to form a plane parallel optical resonator. It is not usually necessary to coat these surfaces to increase their reflectivity, but the other pair of surfaces perpendicular to the junction is often roughened to prevent oscillation in modes which involve reflection. The diodes are roughly cubic in shape with a junction area of about

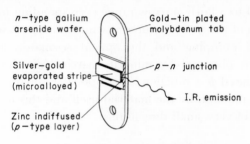

FIG. 10.2   An alternative form of gallium arsenide laser
diode showing the line mesa structure

10^{-3} cm². The active region is the p–n junction whose thickness is approximately equal to the diffusion length of the injected carriers, about $1\ \mu$. Usually the diodes are made by diffusing zinc into n-type wafers with donor concentrations of between 0.6×10^{18} and 5×10^{18} per cm³. The acceptor concentrations are about 10^{19} per cm³. An alternative form of construction, due to Quist et al. (10.3), is shown in Fig. 10.2 which indicates the structure of the line mesa used. In this form the junction has dimensions of about 1.5 mm $\times$ 0.5 mm and the short sides are polished flat and parallel.

The power handling capacity of gallium arsenide laser diodes is small because of the limited heat dissipation available in the junction, and most of the earlier experimental results were obtained near $77°$K using current pulses typically of $0.5\ \mu$s duration at repetition rates between 100 c/s and 1 kc/s. The threshold current densities for gallium arsenide diode lasers usually lie between 800 and 10 000 amperes per cm². Emission occurs in a narrow range near 8400 Å. The form of the variation of the intensity of the emitted radiation with current for a typical diode is shown in Fig. 10.3. At 77°K the radiation in-

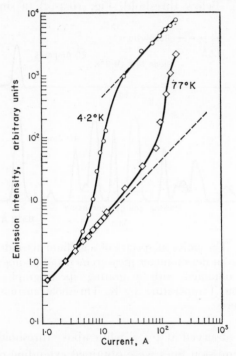

FIG. 10.3   The variation of the light output from a gallium arsenide diode with current at 77°K and 4·2°K

creased linearly with current until a current density of about 10⁴ amperes per cm² (90 amperes) was reached above which it increased rapidly. Lowering the operating temperature to 4·2°K reduced the threshold to 1500 amperes per cm² (12 amperes). At 4·2°K the light output well above threshold again became linear with current and absolute measurements showed that the quantum efficiency of the diode was very nearly unity, i.e. for every electron flowing through the diode nearly one photon was emitted from the polished sides of the junction. In Quist's experiments a peak radiated power of 280 watts was obtained for an input current of 190 amperes.

The spectral form of the infra-red output radiation is shown in Fig. 10.4. Below threshold, Fig. 10.4 (*a*), a single line at

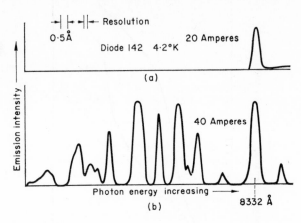

FIG. 10.4   The emission spectra of a gallium arsenide laser determined from densitometer measurements of photographs of the output obtained with a grating spectrograph with 0·2 Å resolution. Temperature 4·2°K. Threshold current just below 20 amperes

8332 Å was observed at 4·2°K while above threshold a number of discrete emission lines were obtained extending over a 20 Å band, Fig. 10.4 (*b*). Line narrowing is observed as the current is increased above threshold. The wavelength spacing of the component lines in the emission spectrum (about 1·1 Å) corresponds to oscillations in modes differing by one-half wavelength in the long direction of the junction. This evidence for coherency was supported by the observation that above threshold the infra-red radiation was emitted almost entirely in the plane of the junction.

Further studies on the radiation patterns of gallium arsenide diode lasers were made by Kingsley and Fenner. A radiation pattern taken in the plane of the junction is shown in Fig. 10.5. Several beams of about 1° width were found together with many narrower beams giving an overall beam width of about 20°. In the plane perpendicular to the junction the radiation lobes have rather greater widths as we can see from Fig. 10.6.

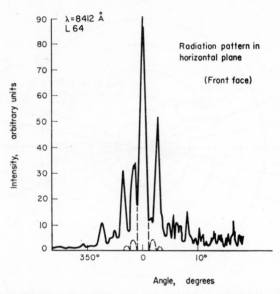

FIG. 10.5   Radiation pattern for one emission wavelength from a gallium arsenide laser measured in the plane of the junction

The narrowing of the emission line with increasing current above threshold, to which we have referred briefly above, is shown in more detail in Fig. 10.7 which refers to conditions well below threshold. At very low currents the width of the spontaneous emission line was 88 Å and this decreased to 26 Å at about 5 amperes. The width is caused by oscillation in several of the modes of the resonator formed by the junction. Just above threshold, when there is sufficient amplification for preferential oscillation to occur in one mode, the intensity of the radiation emitted in that mode increases abruptly with current, Fig. 10.8, changes of intensity of over ten times having been reported for 2% changes in current.

We can see from these descriptions that semiconductor diode lasers offer two distinct attractions as compared with other solid state or gaseous lasers. The first is that, since population inversion is obtained by passing a current through the diode,

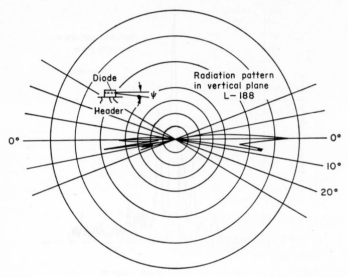

Fig. 10.6 Radiation pattern for one emission wavelength from a gallium arsenide laser measured in the plane perpendicular to the junction

modulation of the output light intensity can be produced simply by modulating the current. Thus there is no need for an independent modulator such as must be used with other forms of laser. The second is that the size of the device is very small compared with that of other forms of laser and thus the semiconductor diodes are very well suited for applications in environments where space restrictions are important. The work on gallium arsenide initiated a search for other semiconducting materials which would also exhibit laser action and preferably

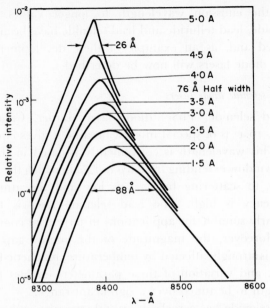

FIG. 10.7 Emission spectra of a gallium arsenide laser
showing line narrowing below threshold

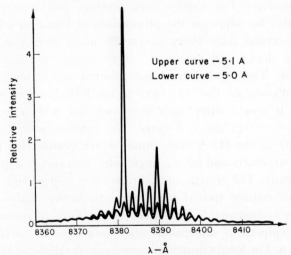

FIG. 10.8 The change in the emission of a gallium arsenide
laser as oscillations begin

179

extend the emission wavelength to longer values. Indium antimonide, lead telluride and lead selenide have been successfully used and, as an example of these developments, lead selenide diode lasers will now be described.

(b) Lead selenide diode lasers

The lead selenide (PbSe) diode laser (Butler, Calawa and Rediker, 10.4) is of special interest because it gives emission at $8 \cdot 5$ μ. This wavelength is conveniently situated in the atmospheric window extending from 8μ to 14μ in which the attenuation due to scattering by haze is low and the atmospheric transparency is high. The lead selenide laser is therefore particularly suitable for applications in terrestrial communications. Moreover, the magnitude of the energy gap in lead selenide is strongly affected by temperature, magnetic field and pressure, and variation of these parameters enables the laser wavelength to be tuned over a significant range.

Lead selenide has a rocksalt crystal structure and is able to exist as a stable compound under fairly wide deviations from stoichiometry. The carrier concentration and type can be controlled by adjusting the proportions of lead and selenium in the crystal since every excess Pb atom gives rise to an electron donor and conversely every excess Se atom to an acceptor. The conduction band minima and valence band maxima occur on the $\langle 111 \rangle$ axis at the Brillouin zone surface and it is thus a direct gap semiconductor with a four-fold minimum energy gap in K-space. This contrasts with the band structure in the III–V compounds which possess zinc blende crystal structures and have a single minimum energy gap at the zone centre. The growth and fabrication of lead selenide diode elements require special techniques. In Butler, Calawa and Rediker's experiments they were in the form of rectangular parallelepipeds of dimensions about $0 \cdot 4 \times 0 \cdot 18 \times 0 \cdot 18$ mm, Fig. 10.9. The longer dimension was made the distance between the parallel reflecting faces which defined the Fabry–Perot resonator. Ohmic contacts were made to the *p*-type PbSe by using evaporated gold and to the *n*-type PbSe with either In or an In–Sn alloy. The laser elements were mounted in special

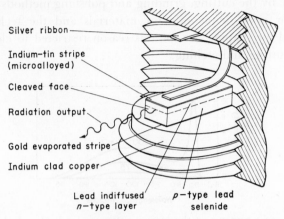

Silver ribbon

Indium–tin stripe
(microalloyed)

Cleaved face

Radiation output

Gold evaporated stripe

Indium clad copper

Lead indiffused
n–type layer

p–type lead
selenide

FIG. 10.9   Constructional details of a lead selenide laser diode

low inductance holders similar to those used in the microwave region; one of these is shown in Fig. 10.10. A point of some technological interest is that the thermal expansion coefficient

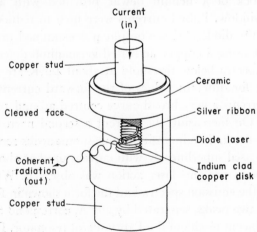

Current
(in)

Copper stud

Ceramic

Cleaved face

Silver ribbon

Diode laser

Coherent
radiation
(out)

Indium clad
copper disk

Copper stud

FIG. 10.10   Low inductance mount for lead selenide laser diode

of lead selenide is comparable with those of the easily machined metals and so packaging for low temperature operation is not difficult. The single crystals are, however, susceptible to damage by the cutting, grinding and polishing methods widely used for other semiconductor materials and the techniques adopted for shaping are for this reason restricted to cleaving, spark-cutting and etching.

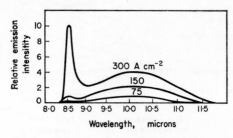

FIG. 10.11   Spectra of the emission from a lead selenide laser at 12°K with forward currents well below threshold

Measurements of the emission spectra were made at low temperatures by mounting the laser diode on the conduction cooled block of a helium dewar provided with a barium fluoride window. Pulsed currents were used to reduce heating effects in the diode and the output was examined in a monochromator using a copper activated germanium detector. The emission spectra below threshold at about 4·2°K are shown in Fig. 10.11 for different values of the forward current density. At low currents a very broad curve centred around 10·1 μ was observed. On increasing the current a second narrower peak formed at 8·5 μ. The intensity of this spontaneous radiation at 8·5 μ increased superlinearly with current until at above about 2000 amperes per cm² laser action was observed. Well above threshold the emission spectra had the form shown in Fig. 10.12 where the two peaks, separated by 287 Å, correspond to oscillation in adjacent modes of the Fabry–Perot resonator. Fig. 10.13 illustrates the variation of emission intensity with current density. Here we can see that the rapid rise at low current densities corresponds to the superlinear behaviour of the spontaneous radiation peak at 8·5 μ. The break in the curve indicated at about 2000 amperes per cm² corresponds to the beginning of laser action and the linear slope at higher current

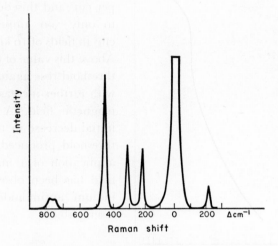

FIG. 10.12 Spectra of coherent infra-red emission from a lead selenide laser at 12°K well above threshold. Forward current density 4000 amperes per cm², diode area 2×10^{-4} cm²

densities indicates that the quantum efficiency reaches a limiting value. This behaviour is in contrast with that of III–V semiconductor diode lasers for which the spontaneous radiation below threshold usually increases linearly with current and superlinear behaviour is generally associated with the start of laser action.

Butler, Calawa and Redika also studied the effect of a magnetic field applied parallel to the direction of flow of current through the diode along a [100] crystallographic direction. A linear shift of the emission peak was observed at a rate of 17 Mc/s per gauss, a result in agreement with the values of magnetic shift for emission associated with band-to-band transitions and predicted from interband magneto-absorption studies (10.5). The application of the magnetic field also affected the threshold for laser action. At zero field, as we have already seen, the threshold was about 2000 amperes per cm^2 and this decreased to only 500 amperes per cm^2 in fields of 10 kilogauss. Above this value of field the threshold rose again slowly with further increase in the magnetic field. A similar initial decrease in the laser threshold produced by the application of a magnetic-field has been observed in indium antimonide diode lasers (10.6).

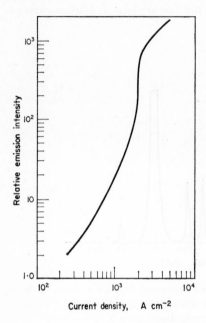

Fig. 10.13 Variation of the intensity of emission from a lead selenide laser with current at 12°K

✳ 10.2 Liquid lasers

There is a group of compounds known collectively as rare earth chelates which have for a long time been known to exhibit extremely intense fluorescence. These form the basis of a class of liquid lasers known as chelate lasers. The chemistry of the chelates is complex and so discussion will be restricted to one of the europium β-diketone chelates which has been shown by Lempicki, Samelson and Brecher (10.7) to exhibit laser action. In the chelates the metallic ion is bonded to six or eight carbonyl oxygen atoms and may co-ordinate with solvent molecules as well. Many β-diketones can be used as chelating

184

agents but benzoylacetonate (B) has been found to be specially useful. The structural formula for benzoylacetone is

$$C_6H_5-\overset{\overset{\textstyle O}{\|}}{C}-CH_2-\overset{\overset{\textstyle O}{\|}}{C}-CH_3$$

The europium chelates can be prepared in solid form either as $EuKe_3$, $EuKe_3.2H_2O$ or in particular $EuKe_4P$, where the symbols Ke and P have been used to represent the chelating agent and the piperidinium ion respectively. In solution the chelates give rise to a variety of molecular species depending on the solvent and a 3 : 1 mixture of ethanol and methanol is particularly useful because it readily dissolves the chelate and has the advantage of glassing at low temperatures.

The chelate solution investigated by Lempicki, Samelson and Brecher was EuB_4P, a europium chelate prepared with benzoylacetonate and dissolved in alcohol to give a europium concentration of about $1\cdot2 \times 10^{19}$ centres per cm^3. A simplified energy level diagram is shown in Fig. 10.14. Here the pumping

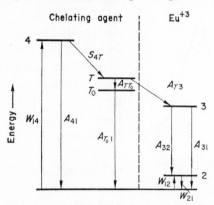

FIG. 10.14 The energy level diagram for a europium chelate. (The levels are: 1, ground state; 2, terminal state of laser transition; 3, upper state of laser transition; 4, excited singlet state of the ligand, T_1T_0, triplet states of the ligand. The A's are transition probabilities and S_{4T} is the inter-system transition probability.)

transition is between the ground state, level 1, and the excited singlet state of the ligand, level 4, and corresponds to a wavelength of 3900 Å. The laser transition occurs at 6130 Å between levels 3 and 2. The levels designated T and T_0 are triplet states

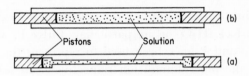

Pistons   Solution

FIG. 10.15   Cells used in chelate laser experiments
(a) 1 mm bore, (b) 4 mm bore

of the ligand and as we can see are coupled both to the upper pumping level and to the upper laser level. One of the difficulties in using liquids is that they contract on cooling to the laser operating temperature and may give voids in the cell containing the solution. This was overcome by using carefully machined pistons, Fig. 10.15, which followed the contraction of the liquid and maintained contact with the chelate solution down to $-160°C$ where the viscosity of the alcohol became so large that voids formed easily. This feature necessitated the operating temperature to be about $-150°C$. Confocal mirror arrangements were used to form an optical resonator and pump energy was supplied by conventional spiral flash tubes surrounding the resonator cell.

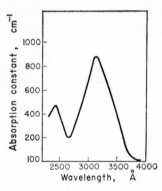

FIG. 10.16   The variation of absorption with wavelenth for a 0·01M solution of EuB₄P in alcohol solvent

Fig. 10.15 also indicates a feature of liquid lasers which is of considerable practical importance. This is that the geometry of the cell, particularly as regards its diameter, has a large influence on the nature of the laser beam emitted. The effect is due to the high optical absorption of europium chelate (Fig. 10.16). The singlet absorption band extends over nearly 1000 Å but, because its peak value is very large (860 cm^{-1} for EuB$_4$P in alcohol solvent), very little pumping excitation penetrates any great depth into the liquid. Thus with small diameter resonator cells as in Fig. 10.15 (a) it was possible to achieve high pumping rates along the axis of the system. Interferometric analysis of the laser beam showed that several longitudinal modes were present and at high energies the whole of the laser aperture was filled with a granular structure. With the large diameter cells the absorption was too severe to obtain appreciable pumping along the axis and emission was confined to an annulus close to the surface.

The threshold characteristics and output energy variation for the EuB$_4$P laser are shown in Fig. 10.17. With the 1 mm

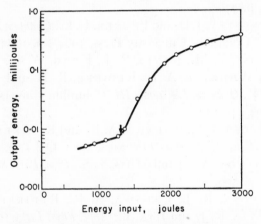

FIG. 10.17   The optical output of a EuB$_4$P chelate laser as a function of the electrical energy input. Cell bore, 1 mm, front mirror transmission 0·1%. Concentration 9 × 10^{18} per cm^3

bore resonator cell the threshold input power required was about 500 joules. This was about half of the threshold energy for a standard ruby laser rod placed in the same flash tube and confocal mirror arrangement. At high input energies the output reached 1 millijoule, representing a maximum energy output from the chelate of about 30 millijoules per cc of solution. This is about four times less than the outputs per unit volume of material which can be obtained with ruby. It is, however, the relatively low threshold (coupled with the output wavelengths available) which makes the chelate lasers attractive. Recent improvements in pumping techniques have enabled room temperature laser operation to be observed in europium chelate (10.8) and this advance makes the laser more competitive as a working device. Laser action has also been observed in a number of other chelates.

References

10.1 BURNS, G. and NATHAN, M. I.: *Proc. I.E.E.E.*, 1964, **52**, p. 770.

10.2 KINGSLEY, J. D. and FENNER, G. E.: *Quantum Electronics III* (Columbia University Press, 1964), p. 1883.

10.3 QUIST, T. M., KEYES, R. J., KRAG, W. E., LAX, B., McWHORTER, A. L., REDIKER, R. H. and ZEIGER, H. J.: *Quantum Electronics III* (Columbia University Press, 1964), p. 1833.

10.4 BUTLER, J. F., CALAWA, A. R. and REDIKER, R. H.: *I.E.E.E. J. Quantum Electronics*, 1965, **QE 1**, p. 4.

10.5 WALTON, A. K. and MOSS, T. S.: *Proc. Phys. Soc.*, 1963, **81**, p. 509.

10.6 PHELAN, R. J., CALAWA, A. R., REDIKER, R. H., KEYES, R. J. and LAX, B.: *Appl. Phys. Lett.*, 1963, **3**, p. 143.

10.7 LEMPICKI, A., SAMUELSON, H. and BRECHER, C.: *Appl. Optics Supplement* 2 (*Chemical Lasers*), 1965, p. 205.

10.8 SAMELSON, H., LEMPICKI, A., BRECHER, C. and BROPHY, V. A.: *Appl. Phys. Lett.*, 1964, **5**, p. 173.

11

Some Laser Applications

In contrast to the amplifier applications of the microwave maser which were outlined in Chapter 6, the main uses for lasers are as oscillators, i.e. sources of radiation. This is because the noise properties of lasers are not nearly so good as their microwave maser counterparts since, at optical wavelengths, the spontaneous emission is so much larger. The properties to be utilized are those of high intensity, coherency, availability of frequency and narrow beam width which characterize laser radiation. No single Chapter can do full justice to the wealth of research activity which has gone and is going into the assessment of the laser's potential range of application. This Chapter attempts to describe only some of the fields in which the laser appears to have a promising long-term future and to mention a few others to indicate the breadth of the current interest.

11.1 Lasers in communications, ranging and navigation

One of the first applications suggested for lasers was in communications where the light beam, being of high frequency, would provide a carrier on which very many audio or VHF channels could be simultaneously transmitted. There has been a great deal of research into methods of modulating and demodulating light beams. Several field trials have been made but recent assessments suggest that for line-of-sight links in the lower atmosphere it is doubtful whether completely reliable communications could be expected at ranges greater than 1 mile. However, the feasibility of a laser over-the-horizon link at distances of up to 100 miles seems more promising. In one proposed system a laser beam would be directed on to a cloud and some of the energy scattered would be picked up by a receiver over the horizon. A relatively large amount of scattering would be expected because of the intense aureole effect present in clouds. Calculations indicate that at a wavelength of 0·7 microns and with a receiving mirror 10 square metres in area the total loss from transmitter to receiver, including scattering, would only be about 114 dB. This order of loss is similar to that encountered in microwave over-the-horizon links using tropospheric scattering which are successfully used for communications over similar distances.

In ranging much more concrete progress has been made. The French National Centre for Space Research and the U.S. Air Force have both used pulsed ruby laser ranging systems with very narrow beams to illuminate and measure distances to the Explorer XXII earth satellite. The former group, using a photo-electric detector to pick up the return signal, found that the distance to the satellite at the time of observation was 1015 miles estimated to an accuracy of within 10 metres. The latter group used a wide-angled camera to obtain a measurement of both position and angle directly on film while the satellite was moving against a background of stars. These achievements show what has been accomplished as regards improved signal-to-noise ratio in these systems and indicate how the position-angle measurements combined with ranging data could be used to obtain extremely accurate estimates of satellite orbits. For use in satellites on the other hand gallium arsenide lasers have the great advantage of compactness. A gallium arsenide laser guidance system has been proposed for rendezvous control of two spacecraft which, it is claimed, would have an acquisition distance of 120 km and provide range information at distances of under 3 km to an accuracy of a few inches.

There are also reports of the use of lasers for optical gyroscopes, in which the frequency difference between two light beams propagating in opposite directions round a closed ring is used as the control. These are used for precision terrain profile plotting, where the phase difference between the transmitted and received laser beams gives range information, and for terrestrial navigation systems.

11.2 Lasers in meteorology

The optical counterpart of radar, called *lidar* (from light detection and ranging) by Collis (11.1), has provided a new technique for the study of atmospheric particles whose size and concentration are too small to be visible on the microwave weather radars, which can detect larger particles of precipitation such as rain, hail and snow. Physically this arises because,

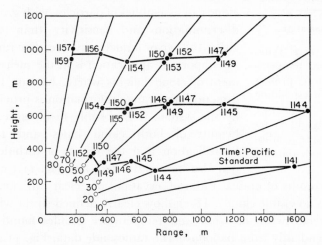

FIG. 11.1   Optical radar observation of stratification in clear air

at optical and near-optical wavelengths, the amount of energy scattered by a small particle is much greater than at microwave wavelengths. The ideas used in the systems are similar to those used in the microwave counterpart but the equipment is of course designed for optical wavelengths. In the optical radars used by the Stanford Research Institute giant pulsed ruby lasers emit pulses with peak powers of up to 30 MW and durations of about 25 ns. The laser is coupled to a telescope to form the transmitter and a separate optical system is used for the receiver. The receiver detects the faint radiation back-scattered from the particles. It consists of photomultipliers from which the noise due to scattered sunlight is excluded by very narrow band filters, giving a system suitable for daylight operation.

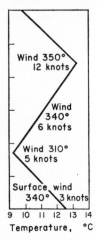

FIG. 11.2 Wind and temperature profiles corresponding to Fig. 15.1 (balloon-borne radiosonde data)

The basic optical radar technique consists of obtaining information on the variation of back scattering from the different parts of the atmosphere visible to the lidar. From this deductions can be made about the nature of clouds, or assemblies of particles, with greater discrimination and sensitivity than with either the eye or a microwave weather radar. An important application is in the measurement of cloud heights where, because both direction and range information is provided by the system, it is possible to measure the heights of both cloud bases and tops. Stratification and the effects of turbulence can also be investigated, and Fig. 11.1 gives the results of optical radar observations on 'clear' air (i.e. air with no visible cloud). These show clearly defined strata which correlate with the wind and temperature profiles found independently from balloon-borne radiosonde data, Fig. 11.2.

Similar equipment, using a Q-switched ruby laser giving a

peak power of 10 MW, has been used at the Radio Research Station, Slough, to study the distribution of atmospheric dust at heights up to about 120 km in order to assess the influence of dust in causing interference in communications.

11.3 Lasers and metrology

In the field of measurements and metrology well-established interferometric methods are being applied with a laser as a source to extend the scale of operation to dimensions previously not possible because of the lack of fringe visibility.

Using a helium–neon laser as an interferometric light source the National Bureau of Standards measured the length of a metre bar to within 7 parts in 10^8. The neon wavelength was found by interferometric comparison, using a mercury lamp generating 436 nanometres as a standard source. This showed the neon wavelength to be 632·819 83 nm under standard conditions. The measurement of the length of the bar was made by moving it over its entire length inside the interferometer and counting the interference fringes formed automatically. The total fringe count of 3 160 460·33 gave the length of the metre bar as 1·000 000 98 m which agreed to within 7 parts in 10^8 with an independent measurement of 1·000 001 05 for the same bar. The interferometer performance was markedly improved using the laser instead of the mercury lamp, and the contrast of the fringe pattern remained constant over the whole length of the bar.

A second example of a laser interferometer is in the measurement of surface profile. An interferometric surface contour projector which is commercially available uses a gas laser as a source and records very small deviations from flatness in surface plates, straight edges and machine ways which have ground and lapped. A similar machine using two interferometers is reported to be able to measure along x and y co-ordinate axes to an accuracy of 0·0004 in and to estimate angular accuracy between the nominally perpendicular directions to within 1 second of arc.

A direct application of the laser's narrow beam width is in instrumentation for testing the alignment of precision slideways on milling machines and jig borers, where in some of the larger machines the slideways may be up to 40 ft in length. In one alignment equipment a cw gas laser is fixed centrally at one end of the slideway and a photocell detector, positioned transversely by a micrometer, is moved along the slide. At present alignment accuracies of about 0·0002 in over distances of 20 ft can be obtained.

A more ambitious alignment application is the attempt to use laser techniques for precise aligning of a 10 000-ft long run of waveguide at the Stanford Linear Accelerator Centre (11.2). The problem here is that this length of guide, forming part of the 20 billion electron volt linear accelerator now under construction, must remain straight to within ± 1 mm over its entire length if the electron trajectories are not to be disturbed. The method of alignment proposed is to direct the beam from a cw laser down the supporting pipe which runs parallel to the waveguide and holds it in place. The laser is excited by r.f. radiation at 40·68 Mc/s and gives a 3 mW output at 6328 Å in a beam of divergence about 0·2 milliradian. Observation stations are located at 40 ft intervals along the beam path and these house square retractable two-dimensional Fresnel zone plates which can be inserted into the laser beam for checking the interference pattern. The Fresnel screens produce images which are scanned by a coherent detector whose output is fed to circuits for analysing the image intensity. Using these as monitors adjustment of the supporting pipe, and hence of the waveguide, is made by electronically controlled jacks.

11.4 Laser machining

Spot-welds of high quality can be made by laser welding of
fine wires (of between about 0·015 in and 0·030 in diameter)
or of fine wire to metal foil. This finds immediate use in connection with the production of miniature and microminiature

Fig. 11.3   (a) A laser weld of 0·002 in diameter copper wires
(Courtesy of the International Research and Development
Company Ltd., Newcastle)

electronic components. This application has been developed
commercially and the principles of one equipment, for which
details have been released (11.3), will be outlined. Here the
beam is obtained from a pulsed ruby laser operating at 6943 Å
and is focused by an optical lens into a spot 0·010 in diameter.
The laser delivers between 5 and 15 joules of energy in pulses
whose duration can be varied between 1 and 4 ms. A mode of

operation known as 'drill-fill' is employed in which the
expulsion of vapourized metal is controlled, so leaving molten
metal to fill in the hole initially formed. As a result of this welds
of high depth-to-width ratios are obtained and it is claimed that
weld strengths of at least 90% of the wires' tensile strength can
be obtained. Fig. 11.3 shows some examples of laser welding
and machining.

FIG. 11.3   (b) Laser drilling of a fine hole through mild steel
(Courtesy of the International Research and Development
Company Ltd., Newcastle)

Another laser machining application that has been suggested
is the precision etching of relief printing plates and we will refer
to the laser engraving system proposed by Reid (11.4). The
ideas involved in this scheme are illustrated diagrammatically
in Fig. 11.4. The basic process is simply a machining operation,
i.e. the removal of metal from the plate, and in this instance
calls for repetitive laser pulses, each pulse burning a cavity of

controlled volume on the surface of the plate. This would provide, for example, a non-printing area for letterpress plates. The laser beam could be made to scan the plate either by the simple means indicated or by a more refined optical system giving a series of craters covering the whole area. The depth and volume of each crater burned into the plate could be

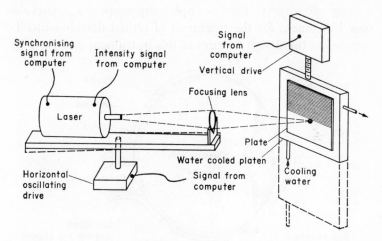

FIG. 11.4   Schematic arrangement for laser etching relief printing plates

controlled by monitoring the energy content of each laser pulse. A computer would be used to control the scanning and laser operation, and this would receive its basic information from, for example, a photocell scanning a photograph or data stored on magnetic tape. Reid estimated that to cover an 8 in × 10 in printing plate in a standard style about 3.3×10^5 laser pulses would be required and that, assuming the depth of etching required was 0.003 in the laser energy required would only be about 0.03 watt second per pulse. This is quite small compared with the values of 350 to 500 watt seconds per pulse which have been reported for many lasers. Compared with conventional methods the laser system offers the advantage of greater operational speed provided that lasers with fairly high-duty cycles become available.

11.5 Applications in surgery and medicine

In addition to the welding of metals by laser beams there is another welding application in an entirely different field, namely eye surgery. The laser ophthalmoscope is a remarkable new instrument for the treatment of retinal detachments. To appreciate the design features of this instrument and the tech-

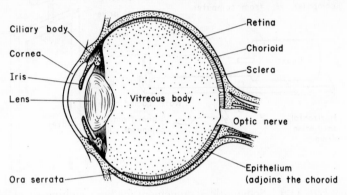

FIG. 11.5   Sectional diagram of the human eye

nique of its use we need to know something of the structure of the eye and of the absorption coefficients for its component media at various optical wavelengths. A sectional diagram of the human eye is shown in Fig. 11.5, and we can see at once that in order to effect treatment of the retina a light beam must pass unabsorbed through the main part of the eye. The eye is, of course, extremely sensitive, and absorption at an appreciable level represents damage which may be permanent. A wavelength which has a very high transmission coefficient in the clear media of the eye must therefore be chosen. Fig. 11.6 gives the percentage transmission through the clear media as a function of wavelength and this shows that for treatment of the retina a wavelength between about 5000 Å and 8000 Å should be used. The emission from the ruby laser at 6943 Å falls within this range, and this is used in the ophthalmoscope described by Smart (11.5). Here the beam from a pulsed ruby laser is directed via an optical system and light pipe into the eye where it forms a spot on the retina whose size can be adjusted by controlling the divergence of the beam and is typically of about

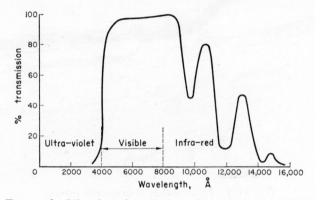

FIG. 11.6   Wavelength variation of optical transmission through the clear media of the eye

10 microns diameter. At energy levels which usually lie between 0·1 and 0·2 joules 'spot-welds' are produced between the retina and the choroid. This is illustrated in Fig. 11.7, which shows a section through a surgical lesion produced by a ruby ophthalmoscope. Although the retina has been detached from the choroid during sectioning the irradiated area has remained firmly welded together. This type of spot-weld is required if a detached retina is to be secured in position once it has been flattened. The spot-welded areas are of course damaged, but their size is so small that vision is not impaired.

Another biomedical application of lasers is in the treatment of certain forms of cancer, where Goldman (11.6) has used laser beams to treat skin cancers which are coloured either naturally or artificially by pigments. In this field, as well as in studies in cellular surgery (made possible by the high radiation density which can be obtained in very small spots), we may expect to see considerable advances.

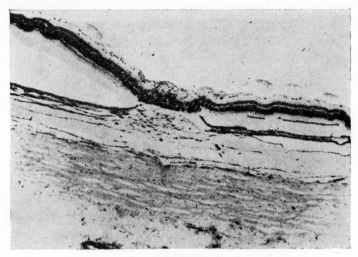

FIG. 11.7   Laser welds of detached retinas

11.6 Chemical applications

There is a completely different field of activity — laser induced chemical reactions — in which such significant results have been reported that we may be fairly certain that much more

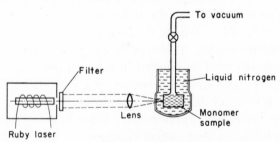

FIG. 11.8   Apparatus for laser polymerization of styrene monomer

will follow. Two examples of these reactions are described below.

The first of these is the polymerization, by Yo Han Pao and Rentzepis (11.7) of a styrene monomer into polystyrene. The system used is shown schematically in Fig. 11.8. Light from a pulsed ruby laser was directed on to a freshly distilled sample

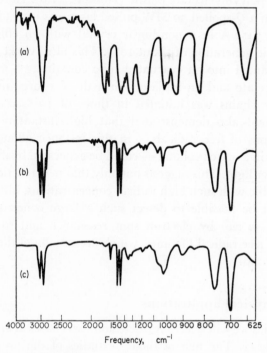

FIG. 11.9 Infra-red spectra of (*a*) styrene monomer, (*b*) commercial polystyrene and (*c*) laser induced polystyrene

of a styrene monomer, which was maintained at 77°K in a liquid nitrogen jacket to stabilize free radicals released in the reaction. Polymerization took place and the infra-red spectra reproduced in Fig. 11.9 show both the effect of laser irradiation and that the product was identical with commercial polystyrene. The polymerization reaction is due to a two-photon process. Two photons, each of energy $1 \cdot 8$ ev corresponding to the laser wavelength of 6940 Å, are absorbed simultaneously by short lifetime excitation states of the molecule. This is made possible by the high photon flux density in the irradiating beam — one of the unique features of the laser.

The second example is the use of an ultra-violet laser beam to form polyvinylacetate plastic (Hoskins, 11.8). Here the output from a Q-spoiled 50 MW pulsed laser was used to produce light at 3472 Å in a non-linear crystal with an efficiency of harmonic generation of about 10%. This ultra-violet light was then beamed into an evacuated tube containing a mixture of vinyl acetate and an initiator. Growth of a large number of polymer chains was initiated in times of 10^{-8} second. The experiment also demonstrated that high instantaneous concentrations of free radicals — in this instance about 10^7 free radicals in a one cc volume — could be generated by irradiation with laser light. This suggests not only that new reactions might be possible with such high radical concentrations, but also that it might be possible to detect such a large concentration of radicals *in vivo* by electron spin resonance and so measure directly free radical lifetimes, which are usually of the order of 10^{-8} second.

11.7 Physical applications

In physics we will select for discussion two classes of application of the laser. The first of these — studies of the properties of coherent light — is a field in which the new experiments, made possible with the advent of high power coherent sources (e.g. 11.9), have prompted a considerable amount of theoretical work on the nature of coherence. It is a subject, however, rather beyond the scope of the present book. The second is the extension of the scope of spectroscopy both as regards the study of weak transitions, where the intensity of a laser source is the attractive feature, and investigations of energy systems requiring wavelengths now becoming available at reasonable power levels by the use of the various gas and solid state lasers, particularly when coupled with a non-linear optical harmonic generator.

An example of the second type of application is provided by the laser-excited Raman spectrometer (11.10) developed for the study of molecular structures and chemical analysis. In observing Raman spectra a highly monochromatic beam of light is directed at a sample, usually a liquid. The resulting scattered radiation consists not only of the original monochromatic light, but also of the very weak Raman lines which differ in wavelength from the incident wave. The frequency difference between the Raman spectra and the exciting source is related to the molecular vibrational frequencies characteristic of the sample. Thus, because it involves a second-order scattering process, Raman spectroscopy offers a possible method for rapid and accurate analysis of mixtures which are difficult to handle by methods involving absorption phenomena. Application of the technique has, however, proved difficult with conventional systems using mercury arc light sources and chemical solution filters to isolate the desired spectral line because of the very low intensities involved. In the laser excited spectrometer a cw helium–neon gas laser is used as a source. On leaving the laser the visible red beam impinges on a glass sample cell which is slightly wedged to produce many traversals of the light and ensure maximum excitation. The scattered light from the cell is focused on to the entrance slits of a monochromator whose output is detected by a photomultiplier and, after amplification, appears as a trace on a chart recorder. An example of this is given in Fig. 11.10, which shows the Raman spectra of carbon tetrachloride, and the clarity of the signals is very apparent. Some other advantages of the laser system, which accrue from the brightness, monochromaticity and polarization of the laser beam, are that photodecomposition of the sample is less likely, that it allows investigation of coloured samples which would normally absorb the shorter wavelengths emitted by a mercury source, and that depolarization experiments are much easier.

It has already been pointed out that the feasibility of laser

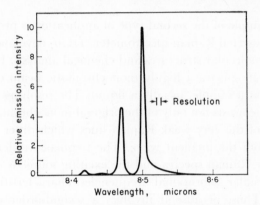

FIG. 11.10 Raman spectra of carbon tetrachloride obtained with a gas laser Raman spectrometer

and maser operation is dependent on the properties of the active material and perhaps the most significant use of lasers and masers will be as tools for exploration of phenomena still hidden in molecules and crystal lattices.

References

11.1 COLLIS, R. T. H.: *New Scientist*, 1965, **27**, p. 27.

11.2 *The Laser Letter* (American Data Processing Inc., Detroit), July/August 1964, p. 8.

11.3 *The Laser Letter* (American Data Processing Inc., Detroit), July/August 1964, p. 4.

11.4 REID, W. T.: *New Scientist*, 1964, **23**, p. 648.

11.5 SMART, D.: *New Scientist*, 1965, **26**, p. 570.

11.6 GOLDMAN, L.: *New Scientist*, 1964, **21**, p. 284.

11.7 YO HAN PAO, Y. H. and RENTZEPIS, P. M.: *The Laser Letter* (American Data Processing Inc., Detroit), 1965, **2**, no. 5, p. 2.

11.8 HOSKINS, R. H.: *The Laser Letter* (American Data Processing Inc., Detroit), 1965, **2**, no. 7, p. 2.

11.9 MANDEL, L.: *Quantum Electronics III* (Columbia University Press, 1964), p. 101.

11.10 *The Laser Letter* (American Data Processing Inc., Detroit), July/August 1964, p. 7.

12

The Growth and Preparation of Laser and Maser Crystals

In the earlier Chapters, which described the physics and some of the techniques of lasers and masers, it has been tacitly assumed that a crystal having the required properties was available. In practice this assumption is not necessarily true and in fact it is more realistic to say that solid state laser and maser devices are feasible only in so far as the properties of the material used for the active element allow. The solution to the problem of providing suitable crystals is thus fundamental to progress in this field.

This Chapter deals with three topics. Firstly, it reviews briefly the overall requirements of laser and maser materials because, although many of these have been introduced and discussed in preceding Chapters, it is useful to have a clear picture of them in mind so that an appreciation of the virtues and defects of the various growth methods may be made. Secondly, it outlines some of the more important methods of growing single crystals. Here we should remember that it may be possible to grow a given material in more than one way, that it is the exception rather than the rule if two different materials can be grown by exactly the same method, and that very frequently the best growth process will incorporate ideas from several others. Thirdly, it considers the principal features involved in the fabrication of specimens for use in lasers and masers from the single crystal material obtained by the growth processes.

12.1 Requirements of laser and maser materials

Two of the primary physical requirements of a crystal for either laser or maser applications are that the energy levels must be such that the material can operate at the requisite pump and signal frequencies and that the spin–spin and spin-lattice relaxation times allow population inversion to be obtained with reasonable pump powers at the working temperature postulated. As these matters have been dealt with in some detail in Chapter 3, it is sufficient here to say that quite a small number of materials appear to fulfil both conditions. Therefore the crystal grower can usually assume that the chemical composition of the material required is known. However, the material must possess a number of other features and it is in meeting these requirements that many of the major problems of crystal growth arise.

As regards the chemical aspects of the material, we should recall, firstly, that magnetically dilute material is usually required. The paramagnetic ion concentration is typically in the range 0·01 to 0·1 atomic per cent, and its value in the single crystal may be critical because of its influence on the relaxation times and linewidths. This means that the addition of the paramagnetic material must be very carefully controlled and that it must enter the host lattice in the correct ionic state.

Secondly, the material should be very pure chemically. For reasons discussed in the following Chapter the crystal should ideally contain nothing except the required paramagnetic ion or ions and the host lattice material. This places stringent requirements on the elimination of impurities both in the original starting materials and at all stages in the growth process since the required concentration of additive is often at trace level and any impurities should be less than, say, 1% of this, i.e. down to a few parts per million.

Thirdly, the material should be homogeneously doped. The paramagnetic additive should be uniformly distributed throughout the whole volume of the crystal. Local concentrations of paramagnetic material (which may arise from a number of causes) lead to increased interactions between adjacent magnetic centres and between nearest neighbours. These in turn lead in general to a reduction in relaxation times causing, in the limit, part of the specimen to become purely absorptive rather than active under operating conditions. In laser material doping homogeneity appears to be especially important since variations in concentration also cause changes in refractive index and hence in optical path length over nominally equal paths traversing different parts of the specimen.

Turning now to the physical aspects, the material should be a perfect single crystal. This is a most important requirement and one which is often very difficult to achieve in practice. We shall defer detailed discussion of this topic (and an explanation of what is meant by the term perfect crystal in this context) to the next Chapter and simply remark here that all kinds of crystalline imperfections are to be avoided as far as possible.

Finally, we must consider the operational requirements of the laser or maser material, i.e. the environment and conditions under which it will be used in a device. Here we can readily see that the crystal size and orientation must be appropriate. The starting-point in these considerations is the design specification of the specimen. This will usually contain requirements on the geometrical size and shape and also on the orientation of the crystallographic axes relative to the specimen faces. We may, for example, think of the centimetric K/X push–pull maser where the specimen may be a rectangular ruby block of size about $\frac{3}{4}$ in $\times$ $\frac{1}{2}$ in $\times$ $\frac{1}{4}$ in with the c-axis inclined at $54° \, 44'$ to one face, or of a typical ruby laser specimen which might be between 2 in and 6 in long and $\frac{1}{4}$ in diameter, having the c-axis along or perpendicular to the long dimension. The general economics of growth suggest that as a working criterion the maximum possible volume of grown crystal should be usable as a specimen. This has two implications, firstly, that growth in a predetermined orientation is preferable, and secondly, as regards the scale on which the whole growth apparatus is constructed.

A second operational feature is that the material should be chemically stable. A fabricated specimen should have a long life and any material which suffers from slow chemical decomposition either because it is naturally slightly unstable or because of reaction with water vapour or atmospheric pollution is not ideal. The refractory oxides are very good in this respect as compared with, say, the ethyl sulphates. Furthermore, the material may be required to withstand repeated cooling to nitrogen and helium temperatures and must also allow cutting, grinding and polishing operations to be performed without fracture, cracking or similar damage. The former requirement implies that a high thermal conductivity is desirable and the latter that the single crystal must be strain-free. Again the refractory oxides are very good compared with the chromi-cyanides or ethyl sulphates, both of which tend to crack on repeated cooling to helium temperatures. The need for a strain free material means, however, either that low temperature gradients must be maintained across the crystal during growth or that the crystal must be subsequently annealed.

We can readily see from this formidable number of desirable properties that it will be unusual for any one material to meet all requirements. In practice a compromise must often be accepted and, since the primary need is for the correct spectroscopic properties, growing techniques must be modified and refined to overcome or at least minimize any inherent intractable properties of the material chosen. The next section describes some of the available techniques for growing single crystals which have been applied to laser and maser materials.

12.2 The growth of single crystals

(a) Water soluble crystals

In this section the term *water soluble crystal* will be used to denote the wide range of materials which are soluble in water or other simple solvents such as chloroform or alcohol. Because of this property single crystals can be grown from slightly super-saturated solutions, a well-known example being the growth of copper sulphate crystals in an open evaporating dish. In the present context, however, a magnetically dilute crystal is usually required, i.e. the paramagnetic ions must be spaced far enough apart in the host lattice for there to be negligible direct coupling between the paramagnetic centres. This can be achieved by growing a mixed crystal from solutions containing a small amount of the paramagnetic salt together with a large amount of a corresponding diamagnetic salt. If the latter is isomorphous with the paramagnetic, i.e. if both materials crystallize in the same form, a mixed crystal can be grown. It is fortunate that diamagnetic isomorphous salts can be found to suit most requirements. Two of the more important maser materials which have been grown in this way are gadolinium ethyl sulphate and potassium chromicyanide. Here the dia-magnetic dilutants are lanthanum ethyl sulphate and potas-sium cobalticyanide respectively. The former mixed crystal, $Gd \cdot La(C_2H_5SO_4)_3.9H_2O$, contains water of crystallization whereas the latter, $K_3[Cr \cdot Co](CN)_6$, does not. The concentra-tion of the paramagnetic ion in the crystal is usually required to be in the range of about 0.01 to 0.1 atomic per cent and it is generally found that this concentration corresponds approxi-mately to the relative concentrations of paramagnetic and diamagnetic salts in the growing solution.

The simplest technique is to grow the mixed crystal by slow

evaporation from slightly supersaturated solution contained in open evaporating dishes. It is, however, advantageous to place the dishes in dessicators to avoid airborne contamination and to include in the dessicators mild drying agents such as calcium chloride to ensure steady evaporation. From the mass of crystals which are obtained it is usually possible to select specimens of up to a few millimetres in size and these are often large enough for many microwave spectrometer studies.

There are, however, three major defects which limit the suitability of the method for the production of the large, high quality crystals required for masers. Firstly, there is no control over the crystallographic orientations in the grown crystals. Secondly, there is a similar lack of control over the crystal habit, which may be critically sensitive to the growth conditions and to the presence of minute traces of impurity in the growing solutions (cf. Buckley, 12.1). Thirdly, nucleation may start at many points and hence the crystal size is limited because the crystals tend to grow into each other.

These defects have been overcome in more refined techniques. Here a small seed crystal is suspended in a large totally enclosed volume of slightly supersaturated solution which is itself contained in a temperature controlled bath. By choosing a suitable seed (which may in fact have been obtained by selection from the small crystals grown by simple evaporation) a large single crystal of predetermined orientation can be grown. The degree of supersaturation of the solution, and hence the growth rate of the single crystal is governed by careful control of the temperature of the outer bath. Thus, for example, the rate of fall of temperature during growth may be programmed to maintain a constant degree of supersaturation, i.e. to balance the depletion of solute in solution caused by growth of the single crystal. The solutions are prepared and maintained in dust-free conditions in order to avoid nucleation at other parts of the growing vessel, and must be efficiently stirred because the solution adjacent to the growing faces, whose concentration is reduced as growth proceeds, must constantly be replaced. The crystal is rotated, usually at a few revolutions per minute, to help to ensure uniformity of growth on all faces. The growing temperature, which is monitored by thermometers controlling the cooling programme, varies with the material being grown but is usually of the order of a few tens of degrees Centigrade.

The choice of the temperature range used in growth is, in several instances, partly determined by the chemical stability of the materials. The growth of gadolinium ethyl sulphate provides an illustration of some of the chemical difficulties which may be encountered. Here the starting materials are rare earth oxides, X_2O_3, where the paramagnetic is Gd_2O_3 and the dilutant La_2O_3. The first stage after weighing is to convert the oxides to ethyl sulphates. Since the oxides do not readily dissolve in hydrochloric acid it is often necessary, firstly, to dissolve in hot sulphuric acid or even potassium hydrogen sulphide, secondly, to add ammonium hydroxide, when the rare earth hydroxide is precipitated, and thirdly, to dissolve this precipitate in hydrochloric acid. The hydroxide may then be evaporated to dryness, keeping excess hydrochloric acid to avoid hydrolysis, and dissolved in minimum quantities of ethyl alcohol or methylated alcohol. If this solution is added to an equimolecular solution of sodium ethyl sulphate dissolved in alcohol sodium chloride is precipitated and the alcoholic ethyl sulphate is left. Decomposition of the ethyl sulphate occurs above about 30°C, and evaporation to dryness must be carried out below this temperature. For the same reason the growing bath temperature must not exceed 30°C and, to avoid crystals growing in needle form, lower temperatures around 10°C are preferable.

In techniques of this kind the growing times vary between a few days and a few weeks, the better quality crystals being obtained with the slower growth rates. Large single crystals can be obtained whose faces, in the cases of some of the alums and potassium chromicobalticyanide, may be up to several inches in size. The homogeneity of doping is good because the solutions of paramagnetic and diamagnetic salts are thoroughly mixed, and the crystals are substantially strain-free since there is no temperature gradient across the growing crystal. Such defects as occur during growth are mainly due to unavoidable nucleation on the growing surfaces and twinning. There is also a tendency for microscopic cracks to develop on removal of the crystal from the growing vessel since, as a class, the water soluble crystals are very soft and it is difficult to avoid subjecting them to a temperature difference at this stage.

(b) Flame fusion methods

The refractory metal oxides, which as a class fulfil most of the requirements discussed previously rather better than water soluble crystals, present many problems in crystal growth. These arise in the first place because they are chemically rather inert, being practically insoluble in water and the common acids, and in the second because of their high melting points, many of which are in the region of 2000°C. Here the material is not a mixed crystal in the same sense as the water soluble isomorphous salts, but is rather to be regarded as a doped crystal in which the paramagnetic centres enter by substitution for the metallic ions of the host lattice. This class includes ruby (Cr^{3+} in Al_2O_3), which is perhaps the most widely used laser and maser material, sapphire (Fe^{3+} in Al_2O_3), chromium-doped rutile (Cr^{3+} in TiO_2) and iron-doped rutile (Fe^{3+} in TiO_2). The flame fusion methods are derived from the well-established Verneuil process (12.2) which has been used for many years for the commercial production of corundum (α-Al_2O_3) and synthetic gemstones. For laser and maser crystal production, however, very strict control of both chemical purity and crystalline quality is required and two alternative approaches, namely growing from powders or from the vapour phase, have been studied in considerable detail. In describing these methods

213

attention will be directed towards the growth of ruby (because of its unique importance), but it must be remembered that the techniques are applicable to other materials provided that account is taken of their differing melting points, volatilities and chemical behaviour.

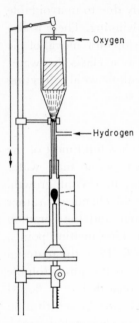

Oxygen

Hydrogen

FIG. 12.1   Diagrammatic representation of a Verneuil furnace

In the Verneuil process powdered material is fed into a flame. The molten particles produced are deposited on to a seed which grows by crystallization from the melt formed on its upper surface. The essentials of the equipment are sketched in Fig. 12.1. The powders, prepared by independent chemical processes (usually as either oxides or hydroxides) and premixed in the appropriate proportions, fall from the container into the flame region generated by the hydrogen–oxygen burner. The seed crystal is mounted on a refractory support (often of quartz) which is usually rotated slowly about a vertical axis and may also be slowly withdrawn in order to keep the growing surface at a fixed position in the flame. For ruby the flame temperature required is about 2050°C. Both the burner design and the rates of supply of hydrogen and oxygen to the flame are important as these factors control not only the temperature near the growing surface but also the environment (i.e. oxidizing or reducing) in which the chemical reactions associated with growth take place.

The commonest form of product is a nearly cylindrical single crystal boule for which typical values of length and diameter are approximately 6 cm and 2 cm respectively. These, together with rods for laser and travelling wave maser applications and other shapes such as discs suitable for window production, are available commercially from several sources. It is noteworthy that the orientation of the boule can be controlled by that of the seed. There is, however, a marked variation of maximum growth rate over the various crystallographic directions, so some are much more difficult to attain than others. In cylindrical boules the most widely occurring orientations are those in which the ruby c-axis is either parallel to the long axis of the boule or inclined at about 67° to it; for these typical growing times are in the region of ten hours. In simple designs, such as those of Fig. 12.1, there is often a large temperature difference between the seed end and the growing surface of the boule. This may amount to as much as about 500°C over a 6 cm long boule and results, as will be seen later, in very considerable strain in the crystal. To overcome this more elaborate furnaces have been designed in which the temperature gradient across the growing boule is reduced to a minimum either by careful shaping of the furnace walls or by introducing a subsidiary heater to maintain the temperature at the seed end of the boule. In this, as with other flame fusion methods, there is often a large difference between the concentration of paramagnetic in the starting materials and that in the resulting single crystal. This arises because the oxides of the paramagnetic and diluent usually have different volatilities at the growing temperature. For ruby, the chromium concentration in the crystal is often between one-half and one-tenth of that in the starting materials.

For the production of high quality crystals several features require careful consideration. The chemical purity of the boule depends largely on that of the starting materials but, since the required concentrations of the paramagnetic ion are only in the region of 0·1 atomic per cent contamination at any stage of growth must be avoided. Here the raw material is a finely divided solid, and this means that it may easily be contaminated during its preparation and subsequent handling. In addition, the materials used for the burners, together with the hydrogen and oxygen supplies, must be free from paramagnetic impurities at trace level. Of these iron, which would enter the boule as Fe^{3+}, is by far the most common and, as it will appear later, one of the most serious.

As regards crystalline quality there are also a number of difficulties. Each powder particle is fused from the outside and so impurities and inclusions inside the particles are melted in.

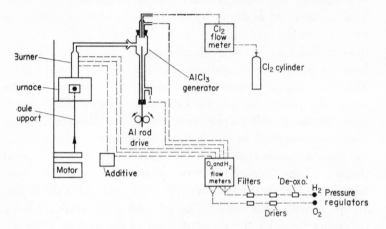

FIG. 12.2   Growth of ruby by vapour phase method from aluminium chloride

The larger particles, moreover, may never be completely melted in the flame and may still have an unfused core when they are deposited. The homogeneity of doping may not be uniform partly because it is difficult to maintain a constant feed-rate of powder and in particular to distribute it uniformly over the growing surface, and also because in feeding mixed oxides there may be localized concentration of one of the constituents. Considerations of this kind contributed in part to the development of the vapour phase method of growth.

In the vapour phase method the vapour of a volatile compound is oxidized or hydrolyzed in a flame to give the required oxide which is then deposited on a seed (Jack, 12.3). Both the chemistry and the technique of growth are more complex than in the complementary powder methods and the case of ruby will be considered in some detail to illustrate the factors involved. The first stage is to generate the appropriate volatile raw material which, for corundum, may be either aluminium chloride or bromide. Aluminium chloride vapour can be made by subliming the pure solid directly into a stream of carrier gas, by direct reaction between chlorine and molten aluminium, or as shown in Fig. 12.2 by chlorination of a high purity aluminium rod fed continuously into a small chlorine flame burning in hydrogen. The reaction is

$$2Al + 3Cl_2 \longrightarrow 2AlCl_3$$

and the chloride sublimes at 180°C. The bromide on the other hand is a liquid between 97°C and 255°C (its melting and boiling points), and controlled vaporization of this probably affords the best means of generating a halide. Fig. 12.3 shows how this can be done. The bromide is maintained at a fixed level in a constant temperature bath and is volatilized by passing a controlled flow of dry hydrogen over it. These figures also show the main features of the growing furnaces. The second stage is the reaction of the hydrogen–oxygen burner flame. It has already been stressed that not only must the flame maintain the growing surface of the crystal within precise limits of size and temperature but also act as the vehicle in which chemical reaction occurs — this makes the burner design critical. One successful design of burner consisted of a series of concentric fused quartz tubes fed with hydrogen and oxygen fuel gases and with vapourized reactants. The optimum design depends critically on the nature of additive constituents and also, for any given additive, on the concentration. The reaction occurring in the flame is that of conversion of the halide to the oxide

e.g. $\qquad 2AlCl_3 + 3H_2O \longrightarrow Al_2O_3 + 6HCl$

P

The paramagnetic constituent (e.g. chromium, iron, titanium or vanadium) is also introduced as a volatile compound fed simultaneously into the flame. In order to make these minor additions the additive compound should be (*a*) unreactive with

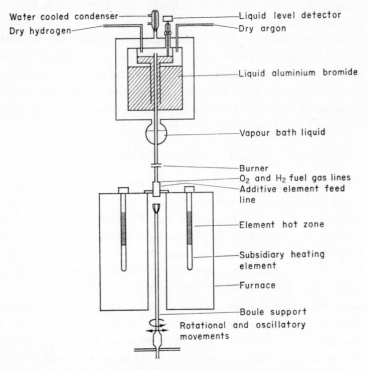

Water cooled condenser——— Liquid level detector
Dry hydrogen——— Dry argon

Liquid aluminium bromide

Vapour bath liquid

Burner
O_2 and H_2 fuel gas lines
Additive element feed line

Element hot zone

Subsidiary heating element

Furnace

Boule support
Rotational and oscillatory movements

FIG. 12.3   Growth of ruby by vapour phase method from aluminium bromide

the aluminium halide until it enters the flame, so that reaction products do not deposit in the burner and feed lines, (*b*) sufficiently volatile at low temperatures to facilitate controlled vapourization and (*c*) stable up the temperatures developed in the burner and until it enters the flame. For chromium and iron the most suitable compounds are chromyl chloride and iron pentacarbonyl. These, however, do not meet all the requirements and in the equipment shown in Figs. 12.2 and 12.3 they are introduced into the flame through water-cooled auxiliary burner tubes. The growing boule is both rotated and moved backwards and forwards relative to the burner in order to compensate for concentration gradients of additive in the

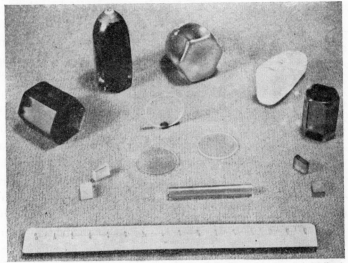

(Courtesy of The Thermal Syndicate Ltd., Wallsend)

FIG. 12.4   Vapour phase ruby and corundum boules with some fabricated specimens

flame and achieve a uniform and homogeneous additive distribution. The inclusion of a subsidiary heating element should be noted because it serves a double purpose. Firstly, it can be used to reduce the temperature difference between the ends of the crystal (which is particularly important for the longer rod-shaped crystals required for laser applications) and secondly, it may in principle be used to enable the crystal to be annealed *in situ* after growth. Some examples of ruby and corundum boules grown from the vapour phase, together with a selection of fabricated specimens, are shown in Fig. 12.4.

(c) *Hydrothermal methods*

Although few minerals are water-soluble at room temperature most of the refractory metal oxides become appreciably soluble at temperatures above 100°C and the hydrothermal growth methods utilize this principle. The method is one of wide applicability and best known through the successful production of large quartz (SiO_2) crystals for piezoelectric oscillator applications (e.g. Brown, Kell and Thomas, 12.4). The several techniques which have been developed are based on the use of a single container, or autoclave, which is heated at the base in order to establish a temperature gradient along its length. The arrangement is shown diagrammatically in Fig. 12.5. The features of the method may be illustrated by reference to quartz production. Here the nutrient, which might, for example, be high purity fused quartz, is dissolved in sodium carbonate solution at the base of the autoclave. The warm solution rises and cools, becoming supersaturated and depositing quartz as a single crystal on the seed suspended near the top of the vessel. (Quartz crystals weighing up to 1 kilogram have been grown by these methods.)

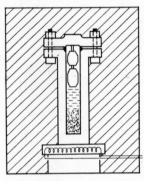

FIG. 12.5 Diagrammatic representation of an autoclave and furnace for hydrothermal growth

The autoclave consists essentially of a substantial metal vessel capable of withstanding internal pressures up to 1000 atmospheres at temperatures which may rise to 500°C. For low temperature work mild steel is satisfactory, but at higher temperatures or whenever corrosion is troublesome stainless steel or nickel–chromium alloys are preferable. The most important feature of the vessels is the method of sealing to withstand the large internal pressures generated. Soft metal gaskets are satisfactory at low pressures, but at higher temperatures and pressures a self-sealing Bridgeman gasket (which becomes more positive as the internal pressure increases) is more suitable (e.g. Paul and Warschauer, 12.5). Conventional designs of furnace are usually adequate since the main requirement is simply that the necessary temperature gradient should be sustained along the length of the autoclave. The internal pressure is usually controlled by the temperature and the initial degree of filling of the autoclave. It may either be measured directly by a pressure gauge or calculated from the published tables for water (Holser and Kennedy, 12.6).

The hydrothermal method has also been adapted for synthesizing a number of gemstones including corundum, ruby, emerald, tourmaline, zircon, and several garnets. The attempts to grow ruby and emerald are of most interest in the present context, largely because the hydrothermal method should in principle yield strain-free crystals. The growth of corundum and ruby have been described in detail by Laudise and Ballman (12.7) who investigated the systems $NaOH–H_2O–Al_2O_3$ and $Na_2CO_3–H_2O–Al_2O_3$. The phase relations for the carbonate system, reproduced in Fig. 12.6, show the ranges of pressure and temperature over which growth occurred. With a temperature differential of 30°C along the length of the autoclave growth rates of between about 0·001 and 0·002 in per day were attained and crystals of several ccs volume obtained. One of the major difficulties in regard to the production of high purity crystals, however, is the risk of corrosion of the autoclave which leads to contamination of the crystal, particularly by iron. Attempts have been made in several laboratories to overcome this by introducing platinum liners in the autoclave, but this raises extreme difficulties regarding the high pressure seals. There is very little published information on the purity and quality of hydrothermal ruby, but the indications are that the method is unlikely to be widely adopted for laser and maser quality crystal production.

The hydrothermal synthesis of emerald, one of the most valuable gemstones, has attracted considerable attention for some years. Small crystals, about 1 cm long and 2–3 mm in diameter, were grown by Nacken (12.8) in 1928 using weakly

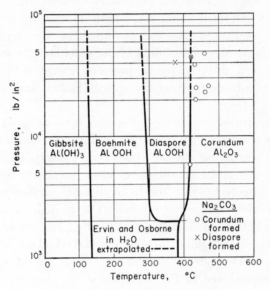

FIG. 12.6   Conditions for hydrothermal growth of corundum

alkaline solutions maintained at temperatures between 370°C and 400°C. More recently Chatham emerald crystals have been produced on a moderately large scale. Full details have not been published, but the process involves the use of crushed beryl as the feed material and the growth rates are reputed to be very slow. Hydrothermal synthesis of beryl from Al_2O_3, SiO_2 and $BeCO_3$ at 400 to 1500 atmospheres and 600°C has also been reported (Wyart and Scavnicar, 12.9). These beryl crystals were transparent and the addition of chromium oxide gave green crystals. For laser and maser use the main disadvantages are the risk of contamination from corrosion, the difficulty of controlling the chromium concentration, the relatively small size of the product and (by maser standards) the poor crystal quality. However, the hydrothermal method appears to be the only one by which this particular material can be grown.

(d) Growth from pure and fluxed melts

Many laser crystals of the fluorite (CaF_2) class are most suitably produced by growth from a pure melt. In the Stockbarger (12.10) technique, from which many of the practical methods are derived, a vertical tubular furnace is divided sharply into a hot upper zone and a cooler lower zone. These zones are separated by an internal baffle which has a hole large enough to permit a crucible to be passed through. The crucible is usually tapered to a point at one end in order to restrict nucleation to a single crystallite. The method consists of melting the starting materials in the hot zone and lowering the crucible into the cooler zone until recrystallization is complete. We may notice that this process is, in principle, simply that of recrystallization and that growth does not depend on chemical reactions taking place. The methods can yield rapid growth rates and large crystal sizes. Control of growth conditions can fairly readily be obtained and since there is no solvent contamination both the purity and quality of the crystals are good. The many crystals grown by these methods include calcium fluoride doped with samarium, uranium and several other rare earth ions together with some doped tungstates.

The fluxed melt process is rather similar. In this method, however, the starting materials are mixed with a suitable flux chosen to give a mixed melt at a reasonable temperature. Slow cooling of the melt causes crystallization and single crystals may be extracted from the mass. The method has been used for making yttrium iron garnet crystals (Nielsen, 12.11) and more recently for corundum and ruby (White, 12.12). In the latter instance good quality corundum crystals, both pure and doped with transition metal oxides, have been produced from solution in lead fluoride. The process was carried out in platinum crucibles heated in conventional furnaces and the crystals produced by spontaneous nucleation on slow cooling formed as hexagonal plates. These plates were up to 3 cm across and, depending on the initial conditions of cooling, up to 1 cm thick in the direction of the c-axis. In the main the crystals grow as truncated trigonal traperohedra bounded by (0001) and $(10\bar{1}1)$ type faces. $(10\bar{1}2)$ faces are occasionally observed, but usually grow out if the growth duration is prolonged. This technique has the advantages that a high concentration of paramagnetic ions can readily be achieved and that the products are substantially strain free, but there is some tendency for the lead fluoride flux to be incorporated as inclusions.

12.3 The preparation of specimens

The single crystal material obtained from growing equipment may appear in a variety of forms. Sometimes growth will have taken place in a particular habit, so that well-defined crystallographic faces are developed. More generally (as, for example, in corundum and rutile single crystal boules) the external shape gives no indication of the directions of the crystallographic axes. An essential preliminary to specimen preparation is therefore the determination of the orientations of these axes in the bulk single crystal. This important topic, which arises in many other branches of solid state physics, will be discussed before considering the cutting, grinding and polishing techniques used in the final stages of specimen preparation. We should note in passing that many of the methods to be described require a considerable quantity of specialized equipment and facilities, and that oriented specimens made to customer's dimensions are commercially available in several materials.

(a) Orientation determination

There is no fixed rule for determining crystal orientations and several optical and X-ray techniques are widely used. Certain of these are relatively simple, but have only limited accuracy and range of applicability, while others apply generally though are more complex both in execution and interpretation. In practice it is common to use a simple method to give an approximate estimate of the position of the axes and a more complicated technique to complete the exact determination. The choice of method depends very largely on the material in question and the facilities available.

A useful start can often be made by means of visual inspection and optical goniometry. If the single crystal has grown in a recognizable habit and exhibits external symmetry a determination of the positions of some of the axes may be made by visual inspection, assuming that the symmetry elements of the crystal class are known from crystallographic data. Thus, referring to the hexagonal-shaped ruby boules shown in Fig. 12.4, it is clear that the crystalline c-axis is lying along the length of the boule. More generally if a crystal (for example, those grown from solution or the melt) has well-developed faces, the angles between these faces may be measured on an optical goniometer. Comparison with tabulated crystallographic data then enables the faces to be indexed and the axes found. This method is illustrated in Fig. 12.7 which shows a typical growth habit of potassium chromi-cobalticyanide together with the interfacial angles taken from Groth's tables.

A second rapid method relies on dichromatic effects. Certain crystals, of which ruby is an important example, show a colour change when white light passes along the optic axis. Thus when a ruby boule is viewed in white light and slowly rotated the colour alters from light pink to dark pink when the incident beam lies in the plane containing the crystalline c-axis, which, in ruby, coincides with the optic axis. This very simple and rapid method defines the plane containing the axis to within about ±5°.

The polarizing microscope also offers a relatively rapid method of finding the optic axis of a specimen providing that

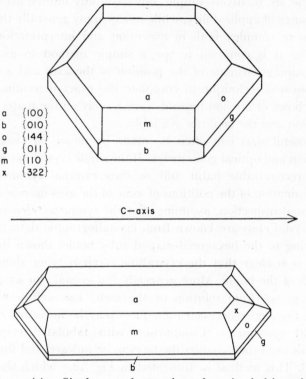

FIG. 12.7(a)   Single crystal potassium chromi-cobalticyanide showing typical growth habits

it is transparent — it is particularly useful for uniaxial crystals. The method consists of orienting the specimen in a beam of plane polarized light until a characteristic cross is observed. This is produced, for a uniaxial crystal, when the incident light is parallel to the optic axis. Further details of the technique and the interpretation of patterns for non-uniaxial crystals may be found in textbooks on optical mineralogy and light (e.g. Kerr,

12.13, Ditchburn, 12.14). We should notice, however, that the patterns can be influenced by strain and defects in the crystal. Under these conditions, which are fairly often encountered in

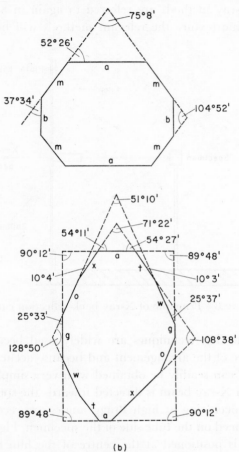

(b)

FIG. 12.7(b) Single crystal potassium chromi-cobalticyanide showing interfacial angles

synthetic crystals, the patterns are not so distinct and interpretation becomes correspondingly less certain.

X-ray methods are perhaps the most versatile for determining the orientation of single crystals because they can be applied to any material, do not depend on the specimen being optically transparent, and can be used equally well for small crystal fragments or large whole boules. Because of this and because X-ray methods are referred to again in Section 14.1 on crystalline texture the relevant methods will be described here.

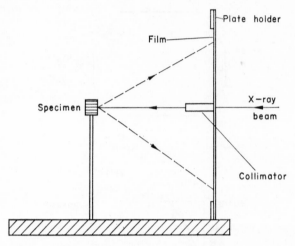

FIG. 12.8   Principle of X-ray back-reflection camera

Back-reflection techniques are widely used because of the convenience of the arrangement and because accuracies of the order of $\frac{1}{2}°$ can readily be obtained with very simple cameras. In these an X-ray beam is directed towards the specimen and reflections occurring at high Bragg angles are recorded on a flat film placed on the tube side of the specimen, Fig. 12.8. The collimator is positioned at the centre of the film holder (the film having a central hole) and it is advantageous if the specimen is mounted on a goniometer head. The specimen–film distance must be accurately known. Camera dimensions vary, but typically the collimator diameter would be about 0·5 mm to 1·0 mm, the specimen–film distance between about 3 cm to 5 cm, and the height of the collimator above the camera base about 5 cm. This means at most an area of only a few square millimetres is illuminated and explains why the method can be used for quite small specimens. Furthermore, since there are no space restrictions on the left-hand side of the specimen support, straightforward adaptations enable large

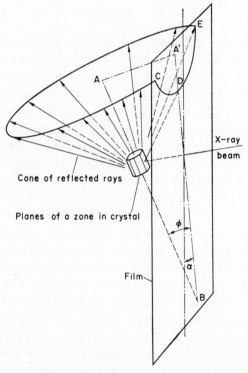

FIG. 12.9   Formation of Laue back-reflection pattern

specimens to be accommodated. The Laue method utilizes a beam of white X-rays so that, with the specimen set at some arbitrary orientation, different lattice planes select an appropriate wavelength for diffraction from the range available in the beam. The formation of the diffraction pattern can be seen from Fig. 12.9. Each zone of planes in the crystal diffracts in directions forming a cone and the recorded Laue spots will be those lying on the hyperbola CDE given by the intersection of the cone and the film. The displacement of the hyperbola from the centre of the film is directly related to the angle of inclination ϕ between the zone axis AB and the film and the closest distance of approach S is given by

$$S = R \tan 2\phi \qquad (12.1)$$

where R is the specimen–film spacing. If the zone axis is parallel to the film the hyperbola degenerates into a line passing through the centre of the film. Thus, in general, the complete pattern consists of Laue spots arranged on intersecting hyperbolae. With the X-ray beam directed parallel to the crystallographic c-axis the symmetry is self-evident, but in the general case it is necessary to assign indices to the zones and prominent spots in order to deduce the orientation. The procedure is simplified by concentrating on the more intense hyperbolae, which are from zones having low indices, and on the Laue spots at intersections, which are reflections from planes common to the principal zones in the crystals. Angular measurements on back reflection photographs are most conveniently made with the aid of Greninger charts which are available for several specimen–film distances. On these the horizontal curves, corresponding to hyperbolae obtained at various inclinations of a zone axis to the film, and vertical curves give the angular displacements between spots on a given hyperbola. If the film is placed centrally over the chart relative rotation will enable any row of Laue spots to be made to coincide with a horizontal hyperbola, Fig. 12.10, and the angles of inclination ϕ and azimuth α can then be measured off directly. Repetition of this procedure enables the angles between all prominent zones to be found. The zones and spots are indexed by comparing the observed angles with those given in tables (for further details see, for example, Barratt, 12.15 or Henry, Lipson and Wooster, 12.16). This indexing procedure can be tedious for non-cubic materials and it is in this respect that previous knowledge of the approximate orientation of the axis helps considerably. Thus if the photograph can be taken with the X-ray beam aligned to within a few degrees of a symmetry axis the photograph shows easily recognizable features and much time can be saved by comparison with standard photographs and stereographic projections.

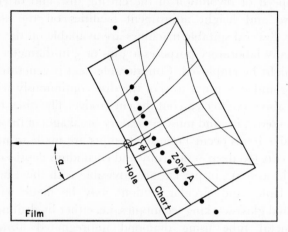

FIG. 12.10   Use of Greninger chart in interpretation of back-reflection photographs

An alternative X-ray method, which is exceedingly rapid, is to use a counter spectrometer with monochromatic radiation. Here it is only necessary to rotate the specimen until a reflection is recorded by the counter, previously set to receive beams diffracted at the known Bragg angle for a given set of planes. This method is particularly suitable for routine control, where large numbers of nominally identical specimens are being handled, but the equipment is necessarily complex.

(b) Cutting, grinding and polishing techniques

Once the orientation of the single crystal is known steps can be taken to cut and prepare a specimen for use in a laser or maser device. In strain-free material cutting does not usually present much difficulty. Soft materials, such as the ethyl sulphates or chromicyanides, may be cut on a simple wire saw and with these it is often not even necessary to use an abrasive providing that the wire is kept moist. For the harder materials such as ruby it is necessary to use diamond-faced cutting and grinding wheels. The essential requirements of a cutting machine are high speed of revolution of the cutting disc and orientation, traverse and height adjustment facilities on the specimen holder. Several suitable machines are available on the market. For many laboratory purposes a 3 in- or 5 in-diameter cutting disc might be employed. Considerable heat is generated while cutting and it is usual to cool the disc continuously with suds which also serve to clean out the cut groove. The discs are quite thin ($\sim$0·015 in) and most laboratory breakages of these rather expensive items occur because attempts are made to make the single cuts too deep — for ruby and corundum depths of about 0·010 in to 0·015 in per cut are advisable with the 3 in or 5 in discs. Holes and circular sections may be made with conventional glass-working techniques, i.e. either by drilling with a soft metal tube using diamond impregnated abrasive or diamond-tipped drills.

In many maser applications the specimen is placed inside a resonant cavity or travelling wave structure. Here the specimen dimensions may not need to be more accurate than, say, $\pm$0·005 in, and the surface finish is not of prime importance. For these a cut specimen is often quite adequate. More exact control of dimensions or finish is, however, required in some instances, for example, where the specimen itself forms a dielectric microwave resonant cavity (as in some versions of the ruby 3 cm push–pull maser) or where etch pit studies are to be made prior to microwave measurements. Here standard metallurgical grinding and polishing techniques can be employed, using diamond-loaded abrasives for the harder materials. The procedure is to grind with successively finer grades of abrasive until the surface is flat enough to pass to a similarly constructed polishing machine. The laps must be perfectly cleaned between stages as scratching occurs very readily if any large particles are included in the grinding paste. In hand grinding and polishing the finish obtained depends considerably on the operator's skill, and the trend is towards automation in order to remove this variable and to be able to handle several specimens at once.

The extension of these techniques to laser rod manufacture warrants some further discussion. Here the basic problem is to produce opposite ends flat and parallel to optical standards, i.e. to at least about $\lambda/40$ and 1 minute respectively. One method (12.3) used for ruby is to cut the boules roughly to shape on a diamond wheel and then grind more nearly to size using a diamond impregnated plate. In hand polishing a cast-iron lap rotating at 5 rev/min is used, and polishing is in three stages using progressively finer diamond. The last finishing stage is on a cast-iron lap covered with fine paper and the total time taken to polish one face is about two hours. In a more refined technique the final mirror finish polish is obtained with a metallurgical vibratory polisher. Here the specimens are mounted with wax on brass blocks and during vibration move around the lap within a retaining rim. The first polishing stage takes four hours per side on a silk cloth lap using fine diamond. The second and final stage also takes four hours and is carried out on nylon velvet with cerium oxide. A similar technique has been reported by Bond (12.17), this makes use of easily adjustable jigs which permit measurements of flatness and parallelism to be made during polishing and thus has the advantage that deviations can be progressively corrected until the surfaces are satisfactory. The optical and interferometric methods used to measure the flatness and parallelism are described in subsequent Chapters.

Q

References

12.1 BUCKLEY, H. E.: *Crystal Growth* (Wiley, 1951).

12.2 VERNEUIL, A. L.: *C.R. Acad. Sci. Paris*, 1902, **135**, p. 791; *Ann. Chim. France*, 1904, **3**, p. 20.

12.3 JACK, K. H.: unpublished communication, 1962.

12.4 BROWN, KELL and THOMAS: *Min. Mag.*, 1952, **29**, p. 858.

12.5 PAUL and WARSCHAUER: *Rev. Sci. Inst.*, 1957, **28**, p. 62.

12.6 HOLSER and KENNEDY: *Amer. J. Sci.*, 1958, **256**, p. 744; *Amer. J. Sci.*, 1959, **257**, p. 71.

12.7 LAUDISE and BALLMAN: *J. Amer. Chem. Soc.*, 1958, **80**, p. 2655.

12.8 NACKEN (see VAN PRAAGH): *Geol. Mag.*, 1947, **84**, p. 98.

12.9 WYART and SCAVNICAR: *Bull. Soc. Franc. Min. Cryst.*, 1957, **80**, p. 3956.

12.10 STOCKBARGER: *Disc. Faraday Soc.*, 1949, **5**, p. 294.

12.11 NIELSEN, S.: *J. Appl. Phys.*, 1958, **29**, p. 390.

12.12 WHITE, E. A. D.: *Nature*, 1961, **191**, p. 901; *Quarterly Rev. Chem. Soc.*, **15**, p. 1.

12.13 KERR, P. F.: *Optical Mineralogy* (McGraw-Hill, 1959), Chapter 6.

12.14 DITCHBURN, R. W.: *Light* (Blackie, 1963), Chapter 16.

12.15 BARRATT, C. S.: *Structure of Metals* (McGraw-Hill, 1943), p. 167 et seq.

12.16 HENRY, N. F. M., LIPSON, H. and WOOSTER, W. A.: *The Interpretation of X-Ray Diffraction Photographs* (Macmillan, 1960), Chapter 6.

12.17 BOND: *Rev. Sci. Inst.*, 1962, **33**, p. 372.

13

Appraisal of Laser and Maser Crystals
I. Chemical Constitution

THE appraisal of laser and maser materials is a subject to which an increasing amount of research has been devoted since the first solid state maser was operated in 1957. The reasons for this trend are not difficult to appreciate and stem from the facts that the device performance is very greatly influenced by the quality of the active material and that, in order to make equipment useful for widespread application, the performance must be reliable and reproducible. Appraisal studies may be broadly divided into two groups where the objectives are primarily (*a*) control of growth and preparation processes in order to obtain material meeting a required specification and (*b*) studying the effects of crystalline defects of all kinds on laser and maser performance with the ultimate aim of being able to specify the best form of material for particular applications. Two of the more important features of the basic single-crystal material are the chemical aspects and physical nature respectively. The former covers such topics as the concentration of the required paramagnetic ion, its homogeneity over the crystal, and the ionic state in which this ion is present in the crystal. The latter includes questions regarding crystalline texture, dislocation densities, single-crystal perfection, and strain. Very many different techniques are being employed to study the various facets of these problems and it is not accidental that most of the published work has to date been concerned with synthetic ruby; this is still perhaps the most widely used material for solid state lasers and masers and despite intensive research still presents many unsolved problems. For this reason the majority of the results discussed refer to ruby, but we should note that many of the appraisal techniques are perfectly general and can be equally well applied to other materials. In this Chapter some methods for the appraisal of chemical constitution are considered.

A fundamental need in interpreting and correlating measurements of the spectroscopic properties of laser and maser materials is to have knowledge of the concentration of required additive in the host lattice and of the presence and nature of impurities. This is an analytical problem in which the concentrations to be determined are at trace level, i.e. about 0.05% or less. Techniques for analysis at this level include microchemical analysis, optical methods, X-ray fluorescence, neutron irradiation analysis and microwave spectroscopy. Some of these, particularly the chemical methods, have been developed to a high degree of refinement in particular fields, for example in metallurgy and for some semiconductor materials. The new problem with maser and laser materials is that in many cases the combination of host lattice and element or elements to be determined occur in ways which prevent various stages of semi-standard methods from being suitable. Understanding of the detail of many of the techniques requires specialist knowledge beyond the scope of an introductory book and the discussion will be confined to outlining and comparing some of the main lines of study.

13.1 Chemical analysis

Most of the purely chemical methods of analysis of laser and maser materials involve two major stages. The first is to convert the material into a coloured soluble form on which the second stage, which is that of estimating the concentrations of the constituents colorimetrically by comparison with carefully prepared standards, can be carried out.

For water-soluble crystals, or materials which can readily be converted to soluble form, many of the analytical procedures developed for the colorimetric determination of, for example, chromium, iron and most of the rare-earth elements at trace level, can be applied fairly directly. These methods have been applied to concentration determinations of chromium in potassium cobalticyanide and gadolinium in lanthanum ethyl sulphate. The analyses are by no means so straightforward, however, in the case of corundum-based crystals. In particular the accurate determinations of chromium and iron in synthetic ruby have proved extremely interesting in that they provide an illustration of how previously unsuspected difficulties come into prominence. The first major difficulty encountered with this material (Al_2O_3) is that it is practically insoluble and the first stage of the breakdown into a soluble form has usually been fusion with molten KOH, Na_2CO_3 or Na_2CO_3/Na_2BO_3. The second is that many synthetic rubies contain iron as an impurity and this interferes with the formation of the chromium compounds required for the colorimetric estimations. Details of a recent analytical technique for chromium and iron determination in maser crystals have been given by Dodson (13.1), who has investigated the influence of different crucible materials on the accuracy of analysis, Table 13.1, and given comparative figures for chromium concentrations in ruby obtained by chemical methods using zirconium crucibles and by spectrographic analysis which, as we can see in Table 13.2, agree closely for a chromium concentration range from 0·01% to 0·9%.

In general terms there are two disadvantages of purely chemical methods. Firstly, they are more suitable for the determination of a particular element than of the ionic state

Table 13.1

Crucible material	Advantages	Disadvantages	Remarks
Carbon	Complete fusion possible	Absorbs trace elements from melt	Not satisfactory
Nickel (commercial grade)	Complete fusion possible	Crucible corrosion by alkali melt introduces unknown quantities of impurities from the crucible into the melt. Cannot be used where Ni is a possible crystal contaminant	Not satisfactory
Specpure nickel. Specpure iron	Complete fusion possible	Crucibles are not readily available, but otherwise are satisfactory, for low temperature KOH fusion	Satisfactory
Platinum	Complete fusion possible	Corrosion of crucible by alkali melt can yield colloidal Pt compounds which can absorb trace metals from the melt very strongly. Pt crucible can retain trace metals from the melt in solid solution, and release these later to a subsequent melt in a completely random fashion	Not satisfactory due to: corrosion of crucible; exchange of trace metals between crucible and melt is unpredictable; and creeping of the melt
Gold (thick-walled, high purity material)	Complete fusion possible. Less corrosion than with Pt	Corrosion increased with use yielding increasing amounts of colloidal gold corrosion products which absorbed trace metals from melt, though less than for platinum. Exchange of trace metals between crucible and melt was as unreliable as for Pt. Especially regarding the long term retention of Fe	Not entirely satisfactory
Silver (thick-walled, high purity material)	Complete fusion possible. Less retention of trace metals by crucible	Considerable corrosion of the crucible, giving interference with this particular analysis due to the difficulty of removing colloidal Ag without losing trace metals	Less retention of trace metals but not entirely satisfactory
Zirconium (commercial grade)		Contains too much Fe ($0 \cdot 1\%$ to 700 p.p.m.) and Cr (150 p.p.m.)	
Zirconium (pure element)	Little or no corrosion. No exchange of trace metals between crucible and melt. Satisfactory recovery on synthetic standards	Needs care in use to prevent surface oxidation	Satisfactory providing crucibles are used under specified conditions

Comparison of crucible materials for crystal breakdown

in which the element occurs, and secondly, that they cannot easily give information about the uniformity of doping over a crystal. As Chapter 15 shows both these features have great importance in relation to device performance. However,

Table 13.2

Sample no.	Chemical Cr (%)	Spectrographic Cr (%)
1	0·91	0·89
2	0·60⎱ 0·59⎰	0·58
3	0·56⎱ 0·54⎰	0·55
4	0·26	0·25
5	0·18	0·15
6	0·053⎱ 0·053⎰	0·052⎱ 0·053⎰
7	0·03	0·029
8	0·022⎱ 0·021⎰	0·02
9	0·026	0·025
10	0·013	0·012
11	0·010⎫ 0·012⎬ 0·012⎭	0·01
12	Very faint, trace 0·0005 or less	Less than 0·01

Chromium analysis of synthetic ruby (chemical)

chemical methods provide a very valuable analytical tool, particularly when undertaken in conjunction with other techniques described in the following sections.

13.2 Optical methods

There is a distinction between the need for an overall survey of impurity content and the accurate determination of the concentration of a particular paramagnetic ion. For the former purpose optical emission spectroscopy has been widely used. This is a technique which has been refined over many years, allows rapid identification of a large number of elements and typically requires a sample of only about 50 milligrams in weight. An example of the spectrographic analysis of a vapour phase ruby is shown in Table 13.3, which illustrates the wealth of information obtainable. The techniques are now so well developed for the quantitative determination of particular elements, e.g. chromium in ruby, that they are often regarded

Table 13.3

Element	Wt. %	Element	Wt. %
Magnesium	0·04	Titanium	0·0015
Iron	0·04	Boron	0·0012
Barium	0·025	Nickel	0·001
Calcium	0·025	Tin	trace, <0·001
Sodium	0·01	Gallium	0·0008
Potassium	0·01	Silver	0·0006
Chromium	0·01	Cadmium	0·0003
Zirconium	0·005	Manganese	0·0003
Lead	0·002		

Spectrographic analysis for impurity elements in low concentration ruby

as standards. However, spectrographic analysis suffers (in common with chemical methods) from the disadvantage that it is destructive and thus the best that one can achieve is an analysis of a piece of crystal adjacent to the specimen used in the laser or maser rather than the specimen itself.

A spectrophotometric method for the quantitative estimation of paramagnetic concentration has been suggested by Dodd, Wood and Barns (13.2). This has the great advantage that it is non-destructive. Dodd, Wood and Barns used the method to determine the chromium concentration in ruby. In principle, the absorption of a light beam passing through the crystal is measured and, if the absorption coefficient at the wavelength used is known, the concentration of paramagnetic centres can be found. The wavelength of the light was chosen to lie in one of the optical absorption bands due to the Cr^{3+} ion. The Beer–

Lambert law states that the transmitted intensity I is related to the incident intensity I_0 by the expression

$$\frac{I}{I_0} = \exp^{(-c_n d\mu)} \qquad (13.1)$$

where μ is the absorption coefficient at the wavelength used, c_n is the concentration and d the length of the light path in the specimen. Rearrangement of equation (13.1) gives

$$\log\frac{I_0}{I} = A = 0.434\mu c_n d \qquad (13.2)$$

or

$$\mu = 2.303\frac{A}{c_n d} \qquad (13.3)$$

where the ratio $\log\frac{I_0}{I}$ is defined as the absorbance A. The chromium concentrations of a series of specimens of different thicknesses were obtained by averaging the results of wet chemical, optical spectrographic and X-ray fluorescent analysis and the absorbencies were measured on a spectrophotometer equipped with polarizers for the broad bands in the blue and green and filters for the red R lines. This enabled the absolute absorption coefficients to be determined and these are shown in Table 13.4 in which the concentrations are expressed as weight per cent Cr_2O_3. We may notice another attractive feature of this technique, namely, that it is potentially suitable for the study of chromium homogeneity since most optical spectrometers utilize quite small beams. At present, however, the number of other materials for which absolute absorption coefficients have been measured is very small.

13.3 X-ray fluorescent analysis

The previous section showed that it was very advantageous if an appraisal technique were non-destructive. The method now

Table 13.4

Sample d (cm), c (wt. % Cr_2O_3)	O1	O2	O3	O4	I*	2	3	4	5	Value from least squares fit	Standard deviation
d (cm)	0·524	0·077	0·042	0·035	1·269	0·640	0·255	0·133	0·054		
c (wt. % Cr_2O_3)	0·051	0·67	1·2	1·5	0·013	0·035	0·014	0·190	0·60		
	±0·006	±0·07	±0·1	±0·2	±0·003	±0·002	±0·005	±0·008	±0·02		
Blue or Y band (24 700 cm^{-1}) (400 mμ) A { $E\perp C_3$	0·658	0·989	1·072	1·020	0·325	0·452	0·579	0·569	0·739		
A { $E\|C_3$	1·194	1·803	2·056	1·909	0·538	0·841	1·183	1·046	1·434		
μ { $E\perp C_3$	56·7	44·2	49·0	44·8	45·4	46·5	45·9	51·9	52·6	47·1	4·4
μ { $E\|C_3$	103	80·5	94·0	83·8	75·2	86·5	93·8	95·3	102	89·0	9·1
Green or U band (18 000 cm^{-1}) (550 mμ) A { $E\perp C_3$	0·658	0·972	1·059	1·000	0·327	0·452	0·572	0·563	0·752		
A { $E\|C_3$	0·212	0·320	0·360	0·341	0·150	0·147	0·209	0·182	0·252		
μ { $E\perp C_3$	56·7	43·4	48·4	43·9	45·8	46·5	45·4	51·3	53·5	47·1	4·4
μ { $E\|C_3$	18·3	14·3	16·4	15·0	21·0	15·1	16·6	16·6	17·9	15·8	2·2

Sample d (cm), c (wt. % Cr_2O_3)†	I	II	Value from least squares fit
d (cm)	6·035	6·040	
c (wt. % Cr_2O_3)	0·062	0·052	
	±0·002	±0·001	
Red R_2 line (14 430 cm^{-1}) A { $E\perp C_3$	0·516	0·510 (axial)	
A { $E\|C_3$	0·124	—	
μ { $E\perp C_3$	3·2	3·8 (axial)	4·4
(690 mμ) μ { $E\|C_3$	0·76	—	0·76
Red R_1 line (14 400 cm^{-1}) A { $E\perp C_3$	0·776	0·756 (axial)	
A { $E\|C_3$	0·057	—	
μ { $E\perp C_3$	4·8	5·6 (axial)	5·1
(690 mμ) μ { $E\|C_3$	0·35	—	0·35

* Poor quality sample.

† Spectrophotometric determination.

Peak absorbencies (A) and absorption coefficients (μ) for the blue and green bands and the red R lines of ruby at $\sim$300°K considered, X-ray fluorescent analysis, possesses this advantage and provides a rapid means of analysis down to quite low concentrations of some elements (e.g. $\sim$0·1% Cr in Al_2O_3). It is again a technique for the detection and estimation of elements rather than the ionic state of elements, but rather larger samples (having faces about 1 cm square in many commercial spectrometers) are required than in the chemical or optical spectrographic methods.

X-ray fluorescent analysis uses one of the basic properties of X-rays discovered many years ago, namely that if a quantum of X-rays of sufficient energy is absorbed by a material, secondary fluorescent radiation will be produced whose wavelength is the same as the characteristic radiation of the material. Thus the principle of the analytical method is that the specimen is placed outside an X-ray tube and bombarded with X-rays. The primary radiation causes the specimen to emit secondary fluorescent radiation (very often the K emission lines of the constituent elements of the specimen) which is analysed for wavelength in a spectrometer. To give maximum intensity of the fluorescent lines, the wavelength of the primary radiation should ideally be just shorter than that of the K absorption edge of the element to be detected. However, since it is impossible to meet this requirement for specimens in which many elements may be present simultaneously, it is common practice to use white radiation from a tungsten target tube run at about 50 kV. The secondary radiation coming from the specimen consists mainly of fluorescent lines but also contains scattered and diffracted primary radiation and Compton scattered components which together form the major component of the background noise and hence determine the sensitivity of the equipment. The simplest form of spectrometer is shown diagrammatically in Fig. 13.1. This uses a flat analysing crystal (usually of sodium chloride or lithium fluoride) and we may note without further detailed comment the use of counter detectors and instrumentation to enable the fluorescent spectra to be printed on a chart recorder. The lines in the fluorescent spectra are identifiable because the Bragg angles for reflection are known and the counter measurements of integrated intensity are used to give quantitative estimates of concentration. Other fluorescent analysis spectrometers achieve greater sensitivity by using the focusing effect of a curved analysing crystal either in transmission or reflection, but the physics of their operation is very similar to that in the simpler version described.

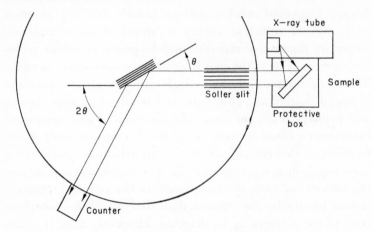

FIG. 13.1   Basic arrangement of components of an X-ray fluorescent spectrometer

Reference back to Dodd, Wood and Barnes' determination of absolute optical absorption coefficients (Section 13.2) shows how fluorescent analysis compares with other analytical methods. Their results for analysis of a range of ruby crystals are reproduced in Table 13.5. In this lattice chromium concentrations as low as 0·01% can be measured by fluorescent analysis and there is good agreement between the different methods. We should note also that X-ray fluorescent analysis forms an important part of the electron probe microanalysis technique which is discussed later.

Table 13.5

Sample	Wet chemical*	X-ray fluorescence†	Emission spectrographic*	Average	Estimated av % error
01		0·061 ± 0·004	0·041 ± 0·008	0·051 ± 0·006	±12
02		0·67 ± 0·01	0·66 ± 0·13	0·67 ± 0·07	±10
03		1·15 ± 0·01	1·2 ± 0·2	1·2 ± 0·1	± 8·3
04		1·39 ± 0·01	1·6 ± 0·3	1·5 ± 0·2	±13
1	0·016 ± 0·001	0·010 ± 0·004		0·013 ± 0·003	±23
2	0·038 ± 0·002	0·032 ± 0·004		0·035 ± 0·002	± 5·7
3	0·110 ± 0·006	0·118 ± 0·004		0·114 ± 0·005	± 4·4
4	0·193 ± 0·010	0·187 ± 0·006		0·190 ± 0·008	± 4·2
5	0·59 ± 0·03	0·61 ± 0·01		0·60 ± 0·02	± 3·3

* The error is an estimate of reproducibility.
† The error is three times the standard deviation.

Comparison of chromium determinations in ruby made by X-ray fluorescent, chemical and spectrographic analysis

13.4 Electron spin resonance

Microwave techniques are more suitable for studying maser rather than laser materials because the transitions involved in maser action correspond to microwave wavelengths and so are directly observable. It is therefore worthwhile to recall the main features required in a maser material in order to see the extent to which these may be studied by microwave spectro-meter techniques. In addition to the over-riding conditions that the maser crystals should be capable of growth in single crystal form, possess the correct energy level scheme for the frequencies at which it is to be operated and have a reasonable relaxation time, a number of other properties are desirable if optimum maser performance is to be achieved. In the first place, the concentration of the required paramagnetic ion should be accurately controlled since this determines the absorption line width and hence influences the bandwidth obtainable in any maser device; it can also affect the spin-lattice relaxation time and may alter the pumping power required for maser operation at a given temperature. Secondly, the crystal should be free from unwanted paramagnetic impurities whose absorption lines coincide with or are very close to those of the required paramagnetic ion. If such impurities were present it would be

possible for pump power to be wasted by saturating an unwanted transition, or for the relaxation time of the required
transition to be seriously reduced by spin–spin coupling to an
impurity transition having a very short relaxation time.
Microwave spectrometer techniques are particularly suitable
as a means for studying these features, because measurements
can be made under conditions similar to those experienced in
maser operation — this unique feature distinguishes the method
from most other appraisal techniques. Moreover, in addition
to enabling concentration and impurity studies to be made,
they are useful in supplying more information on the effects of
crystalline perfection than can readily be obtained from visual
inspection or simple polarized light or X-ray techniques.

Microwave studies of the impurity content of a selection of
synthetic rubies have been reported by Thorp et al. (13.3).
Here measurements were made with an 8 mm spectrometer
using techniques similar to those described in Chapter 3.
Within the fairly wide limits imposed by the ability to see
transitions with a material of given zero field splitting the
frequency of measurement is of secondary importance. On the
other hand, the temperature should be either that at which the
material is to exhibit maser action or preferably lower, since if
impurities whose transitions have very short relaxation times
are present they will remain undetected at high temperatures,
e.g. room temperature of $77°K$, as their absorption lines may
be too broad to be visible. The measurements reported were
made at $1·3°K$ and the polar angle $\theta = 90°$ was chosen in
order to simplify interpretation of the spectra and enable
comparison with previous experiments on adiabatic rapid
passage in similar ruby samples (Thorp et al., 13.4) to be made.
The magnetic field values at which transitions occurred and
their relative peak intensities were recorded.

The results obtained illustrate the potentialities of the
spectrometer technique and the way in which correlation with
results from other methods can be made and therefore will be

considered in some detail. The methods of growth and nominal concentrations of the samples investigated are given in Table 13.6. We should notice that all the crystals examined were not in the fully annealed state, and must also bear in mind the point that the samples on which results were quoted were chosen to illustrate effects which may arise during the develop-

Table 13.6

Sample	Material	Remarks
P1	Ruby	Nominal 0·1% Cr ruby. Grown from powder by a flame fusion method.
P2	Undoped Al_2O_3	Starting material for P1. Grown by same method.
V1	Ruby	Nominal 0·1% Cr ruby. Grown from vapour phase; Method I.
V2	Undoped Al_2O_3	Starting material for V1. Grown by same method.
V3	Ruby	Nominal 0·1% Cr ruby. Grown from vapour phase; Method II.
V4	Undoped Al_2O_3	Starting material for V3. Grown by same method.

Growth methods used in preparation of rubies examined by electron spin resonance

ment of growth techniques and do not necessarily represent the quality of crystal which may ultimately be obtainable by the various growth processes. Typical spectrometer results on some of the samples listed above are shown in Figs. 13.2 and 13.3. In these the field values at which absorption lines occurred are given, together with their relative peak intensities plotted on a dB scale in which 0 dB corresponds to the noise level. In these Figures no attempt is made to indicate linewidth, but where a transition consisted of a resolved close doublet it is represented as two close vertical lines. Where possible the lines were identified by comparison with the known spectra of chromium (Geusic, 13.5) and iron (Bogle and Symmons, 13.6)

247

in aluminuim oxide. The iron lines could be uniquely identified because there are two non-equivalent Fe^{3+} ions in the unit cell and rotation of the magnetic field separated each line into a

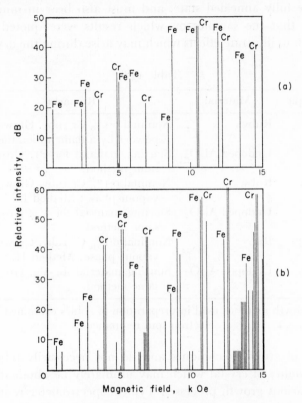

FIG. 13.2   E.s.r. spectra of rubies grown by flame fusion from powder

(a) Undoped aluminium oxide P2
(b) Ruby P1

Orientation $\theta = 90°$, frequency 34·6 Gc/s, temperature 4°K

doublet, except at the symmetrical orientations giving coincidences. Samples V3 and V4 gave spectra almost identical to V1 and V2 respectively. The most striking feature is the comparative freedom from iron contamination in the crystals grown from the vapour phase, since both samples V1 and V3 were found to contain very little iron and no other detectable impurity. In these samples (V1 and V3) the maximum intensity of an iron transition is some 600 times (28 dB) less than that of

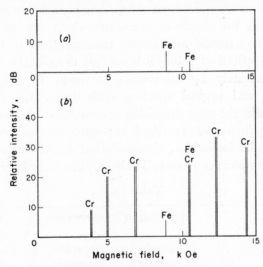

FIG. 13.3   E.s.r. spectra of rubies grown from the vapour phase

(a) Undoped aluminium oxide V2
(b) Ruby V1

Orientation $\theta = 90°$, frequency 34·6 Gc/s, temperature 4°K

the main chromium transitions. The sample P1, however, grown by flame fusion from powder, contains iron in considerably greater quantities and, in fact, shows Fe^{3+} transitions whose intensities are almost equal to those of some of the chromium lines. In addition, this sample gave numerous additional lines, some of significant intensity, which have not been identified. It is interesting to note the close correlation in the intensities of the Fe^{3+} spectra obtained from corresponding 'pure' and doped samples.

R

The spectra given in Figs. 13.2 and 13.3 show that micro-wave spectrometer techniques form a sensitive means of detecting paramagnetic impurities. The method of identifying their nature by comparison is, however, limited to those ions whose paramagnetic properties in the host lattice are known. Hence a major requirement is for a complementary method of determining the nature of impurities which may be present. This method should also enable concentrations to be determined quantitatively, since it is not easy to make this measurement accurately by microwave methods. In this respect chemical and optical spectrographic techniques described already offer the most promising approach, with polarigraphic and X-ray fluorescence methods as possible alternatives suitable for particular impurities. The analytical results for the studied series of samples are given in Table 13.7 in which the chromium

Table 13.7

| Sample | Chromium concentration | | Iron concentration |
	Chemical (atomic per cent)	Spectro-graphic (atomic per cent)	Chemical (atomic per cent)
P1 ruby	0·038	0·033	0·035
P2 undoped Al_2O_3	<0·001	<0·005	0·039
V1 ruby	0·023	0·025	0·004
V2 undoped Al_2O_3	<0·001	<0·005	0·004
V3 ruby	0·011	0·008	0·004
V4 undoped Al_2O_3	<0·001	<0·005	0·004

Analytical data for rubies examined by electron spin resonance

and iron concentrations are expressed as atomic percentages, i.e. the number of Cr or Fe atoms per 100 molecules of Al_2O_3. These were derived from the weight percentages by multiplication by half the molecular weight of Al_2O_3 and by division by the atomic weights of chromium and iron respectively. It may be noted that the chromium concentrations in all the ruby samples are considerably smaller than the nominal concentrations, based on the proportions of additive to host in the starting materials, quoted in Table 13.5. It also appears that samples of the same nominal concentration, grown by different methods, yield true chromium concentrations which may differ by a factor of about three. The difference between the nominal and true concentration arises from the difference in volatility of the host lattice material and the added paramagnetic material at the growing temperature, and the factor of three indicates the extent to which this may be influenced by various conditions of growth.

The spectra of Figs. 13.2 and 13.3 were obtained primarily to detect and identify impurities. Thus, although the samples were of approximately the same volume and measurements were taken under similar conditions of coupling and receiver gain, further information regarding individual linewidths and transition probabilities is necessary to enable detailed quantitative correlation with the analytical results to be made. The peak intensities observed can, however, be used to make some approximate comparisons. For example, in the crystals grown from the vapour phase the iron content of the undoped Al_2O_3 (V2, Fe, 0·004%) gave a maximum peak intensity about 5 dB above noise, this remained about the same in the corresponding ruby (V1, Fe, 0·004%; Cr, 0·024%) giving an intensity difference of about 28 dB between the strongest chromium and iron transitions. In the crystals grown from powder the intensities of the corresponding iron transitions in both the undoped Al_2O_3 (P2, Fe, 0·039%) and ruby (P1, Fe, 0·039%; Cr, 0·035%) were about 43 dB above noise. Both techniques thus indicated that the crystals grown from the vapour phase contained less iron than those grown from powder, and that the iron content of the rubies was substantially independent of the addition of chromium. They could not, however, differentiate between contamination which arose from impurities present in the starting materials and those entering during

251

growth. The difference in peak intensity of about 38 dB between corresponding iron transitions in P2 and V2 was considerably greater than expected from the ratio of their iron concentrations, and this suggested that there might be a significant difference between the amount of iron estimated analytically and that entering the lattice as Fe^{3+}. The paramagnetic spectra also showed variations in the relative intensities of transitions due to the same ion, and these were more pronounced for Fe^{3+} than Cr^{3+}. We can see from this that the information which can be derived from the paramagnetic spectra is directly relevant to crystal growth procedures and that systematic study of samples grown under known conditions would be valuable in establishing growth techniques for very high purity crystals.

13.5 Electron probe microanalysis

The preceding Sections have shown the importance of knowing the nature, concentration and ionic state of the paramagnetic centres present in the laser or maser crystal. This information, though necessary, is not always sufficient to enable the properties of a particular crystal specimen to be specified. For reasons which are dealt with in a later Chapter the uniformity of doping, i.e. the degree to which the concentration of the required paramagnetic centres is constant throughout the crystal volume, is very important, particularly in laser crystals.

In electron probe microanalysis (a technique first described by Castaing, 13.7) a combination of electron-optical and X-ray methods enable quantitative analyses of a very small volume of material to be made. The basic principle is to bombard the specimen with a finely collimated beam of high energy electrons and to analyse the characteristic X-radiation produced by the constituent elements of the specimen using means similar to those described in the previous section. Electron optical and counter detector techniques have been so refined that quantitative analyses for elements at trace level are now possible on

specimen areas of a few microns in diameter — further instrumental details have been given by Dils, Zeitz, Kieth and
Huggins (13.8).

We are concerned here rather with the use of the technique
and we will refer to a study of the distribution of chromium
in synthetic ruby crystals made by Dils, Martin and Huggins

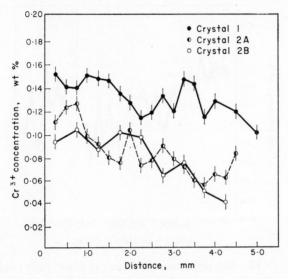

FIG. 13.4 Electron probe microanalysis of ruby; chromium concentration variations in the plane normal to the growth axis

(13.9). In this the crystals were prepared for analysis by normal
metallurgical polishing followed by the evaporation of a thin
metallic film over the polished surface to prevent charge
building up on the specimen. Analyses were made on the plane
normal to the growth direction with a 25 kV electron beam
focused on to a spot $1 \cdot 5 \, \mu$ diameter. The characteristic X-radiation excited by the beam was examined using a standard X-ray
counter spectrometer with a curved sodium chloride analysing
crystal. Scanning experiments were made along various
directions on the polished surface and some of the chromium

concentration profiles are shown in Fig. 13.4. We can see from this that the scatter in chromium concentration obtained during traversing a particular direction is well outside experimental error. There are in fact large fluctuations in the chromium content, as well as an overall decrease in chromium

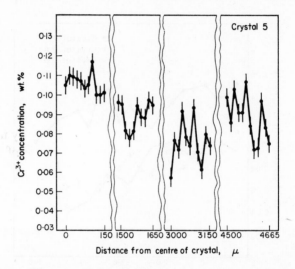

FIG. 13.5   Electron probe microanalysis of ruby; high resolution scans showing detail of concentration fluctuations

level from the centre to the periphery of the Verneuil grown crystal. In vapour phase rubies the reverse trend is found, and the explanation proposed for this difference is that it is due to difference in burner design and feed methods in the two processes. The local fluctuations in chromium content are much more evident on scans taken at higher linear resolution, Fig. 13.5. Here there is, for example, a crystal region in which an enormous change from 0·055% to nearly 0·091% occurs in distance of about 100 μ. As the main interest in this Chapter is in giving some account of techniques the significance of these results will be discussed fully later. There is some evidence

254

(Thorp, Curtis and Mason, 13.10) which suggests that the highest chromium concentrations are to be found near those crystalline regions having the greater dislocation density.

References

13.1 DODSON, E. M.: *Anal. Chem.*, 1962, **34**, p. 966.
13.2 DODD, D. M., WOOD, D. L. and BARNES, R. L.: *J.A.P.*, 1964, **35**, p. 1183.
13.3 THORP, J. S., PACE, J. H. and SAMPSON, D. F.: *B.J.A.P.*, 1961, **12**, 705.
13.4 THORP, J. S., PACE, J. H. and SAMPSON, D. F.: *J. Elec. and Control*, 1961, **10**, p. 13.
13.5 GEUSIC, J. E.: *Phys. Rev.*, 1956, **102**, p. 1252.
13.6 BOGLE, G. and SYMMONS, H. F.: *Proc. Phys. Soc.*, 1959, **73**, p. 531.
13.7 CASTAING, R.: *Adv. in Elect. and Elect. Phys.*, 1960, **13**, p. 317.
13.8 DILS, R. R., ZEITZ, L., KIETH, D. L. and HUGGINS, R. A.: *Rev. Sci. Inst.*, 1961, **32**, p. 1040.
13.9 DILS, R. R., MARTIN, G. W. and HUGGINS, R. A.: *App. Phys. Letters*, 1962, **1**, p. 75.
13.10 THORP, J. S., CURTIS, D. A. and MASON, D. R.: *B.J.A.P.*, 1964, **15**, p. 775.

14

Appraisal of Laser and Maser Crystals
II. Crystalline Texture

II. CRYSTALLINE TEXTURE

In this Chapter the term crystalline texture is used quite generally to include effects such as lattice strain, grain boundaries, axis misorientations, mosaic structure and dislocation density. All synthetic crystals show these features to a greater or lesser degree and material which is spoken of as 'single crystal quality' may in fact be quite unsuitable for meeting the exacting requirements of, say, laser operation. There are many reasons for the occurrence of crystalline imperfections. Two particularly important examples of these are the difficulty of controlling temperature gradients during the growth process, particularly in high melting point materials, and the fact that impurity atoms, being misfits in the lattice because of their different ionic radii, give rise to localized lattice defects. The purpose here, however, is to describe some of the techniques by which the degree of textural imperfection present in laser and maser crystals may be assessed and in doing so indicate the scale on which these defects are commonly found in material used for devices. Again X-ray, optical and electron spin resonance methods are the main appraisal tools, but etching techniques also come into prominence and specialized appraisal methods are continually being developed.

14.1 X-ray and etching methods

The use of X-rays in orientation determination was mentioned in Chapter 12. It is commonly found in fairly large crystals that (a) the lattice is strained, (b) the direction of the crystallographic axes 'wander' throughout the crystal and (c) the crystal may have mosaic structure. These features are particularly suitable for X-ray examination.

One of the simplest X-ray methods, and the only one which will be discussed here, is the back reflection Laue method. This has been used extensively and some of the results obtained by Thorp and Curtis (14.1) indicate the sort of information which may be obtained. Here detailed studies of vapour phase ruby and sapphire were made by back reflection X-ray methods with a camera equipped with a goniometer head so that the specimen could not only be set at any angle to the incident beam but also translated without alteration of angular position. The film was covered with a sectored disc enabling comparative photographs of different parts of a specimen to be obtained on one film. In any exposure, however, the amount of specimen examined was limited to a volume whose area equalled the diameter of the beam at the specimen, in this case about 0·25 mm, and whose depth was only a few hundred atomic layers.

Each back reflection photograph can give information regarding the orientation of the crystalline axes in the volume irradiated, the nature of any mosaic texture and the extent of strain in the crystal or mosaic elements. If the crystal is a perfect single crystal the spots on the film are reflections by the lattice planes of the collimated X-ray beam. The size and shape of each reflection is thus calculable from the camera geometry. An example of this is shown in Fig. 14.1 which refers to a nearly perfect section of vapour phase ruby. If, however, the specimen is mosaic, instead of there being one diffraction spot produced by a set of planes of the same Miller indices there will

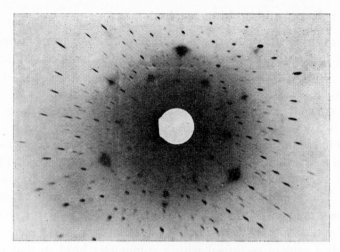

FIG. 14.1 Back-reflection X-ray photograph of single crystal
ruby. Beam parallel to c-axis, CuKα radiation

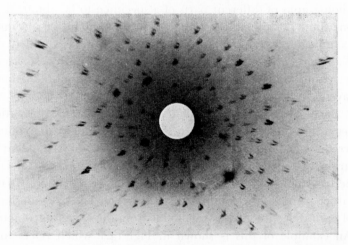

FIG. 14.2 Back-reflection X-ray photograph of ruby showing
mosaic imperfection. Beam parallel to c-axis, CuKα radiation

be a cluster of spots, one from each mosaic element having a slightly different orientation from its neighbour. In this case the range of misorientation in the mosaic can be found from the separation of the components and an estimate of the mosaic element size from the number of components observed and the volume irradiated. This type of photograph is shown in Fig. 14.2. The extent to which the diffraction spots are distorted and broadened beyond the geometrical shape indicates the presence of strain in the lattice. One important factor in the interpretation was to demonstrate that photographs taken of such small volumes were respresentative of the surrounding material. This was achieved by etching to remove about 0·004 in of material, equivalent to several hundred times the depths of penetration of the X-ray beam. Photographs of corresponding points taken before and after etching showed no significant charge in the diffraction pattern. Table 14.1 gives some of the details which were derived (misorientations of about these amounts are fairly often encountered in this material).

The question of dislocation density, which is often taken as a criterion of crystal quality, may be considered next. This is usually obtained here, as throughout a wide range of materials in metallurgy and solid state physics, by etching a polished crystallographic face of the specimen and counting the number of etch pits per unit area observed. Generally speaking, each material requires a particular etchant. Some of the points which arise can be illustrated by reference to Curtis' work (14.2) on ruby and sapphire. Curtis followed Scheuplein and Gibbs' methods (14.3). The polished (0001) faces were cleaned by immersing them for several hours in benzene, then in nitric acid and finally by washing in distilled water. The etching was performed by placing the specimen in ortho-phosphoric acid, heating up to 320°C and pouring away the acid immediately this temperature was reached. In order to ensure that etching took place at 320°C (the optimum temperature) allowance was made for the heat loss in the stem of the thermometer. Etching did not take place if the polished surface was inclined at an angle of more than 5° away from the (0001) plane. Fig. 14.3 shows a photograph of randomly distributed etch pits at a

Table 14.1

Boule 3

(a) Unannealed: end face of whole boule

Photograph reference	Mosaic mis-orientation	Difference	c-axis variation From photographs
3.1 a Edge 1	2° 10′	2° 10′	3.1 a and 3.1 b
3.1 b Centre	1° 30′	1° 10′	3.1 b and 3.1 c
3.1 c Edge 2	No mosaic	1° 55′	3.1 c and 3.1 a

(b) Annealed at between 1850°C and 1900°C; same end face of whole boules examined; positions correspond approximately

3.2 a Edge 1	1° 20′	1° 35′	3.2 a and 3.2 b
3.2 b Centre	1° 45′	1° 45′	3.2 b and 3.2 c
3.2 c Edge 2	1° 30′	3° 10′	3.2 c and 3.2 a

Boule 4

(a) Unannealed, cleaved and cut into slices

4.1 Edge of slice	No mosaic	1° 0′	4.1 and 4.2
4.2 Centre	No mosaic	0° 15′	4.2 and 4.3
4.3 Other edge	No mosaic	0° 45′	4.3 and 4.1

(b) This slice annealed at 1700°C and re-examined; positions correspond approximately

4.4 a Edge	No mosaic	0° 30′	4.4 a and 4.4 b
4.4 b Centre	No mosaic	0° 45′	4.4 b and 4.4 c
4.4 c Other edge	No mosaic	0° 15′	4.4 c and 4.4 a

Estimates of c-axis variation and mosaic misorientation in some ruby specimens before and after annealing

density of 2×10^5 per cm^2 and Fig. 14.4 shows rows of etch pits, related to rows of dislocations forming grain boundary walls, which had linear densities estimated to be about 5×10^3 per cm. We can see from these Figures that the etching method

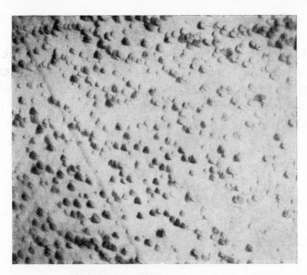

FIG. 14.3   Randomly distributed etch pits on (0001)
face of ruby. Magnification × 16

FIG. 14.4   Etch pit formation near grain boundaries,
ruby (0001) face. Magnification × 160

can give information regarding sub-structure and boundaries as well as the average etch pit density itself.

In interpreting etch pit photographs care must be taken to ascertain the relationship between the etch pit density and the dislocation density and indeed to specify which sets of dislocations are being observed. It is here that X-ray methods prove useful. Of these one of the simplest is the back reflection tech-

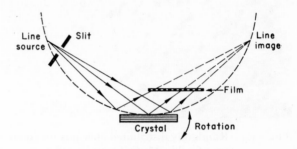

FIG. 14.5   Geometrical arrangement for X-ray topography

nique referred to previously. In this method, which is useful over a density range of about 10^3–10^5 per cm², the angular misorientation α between neighbouring grains and the average linear dimension t of the grains may be found from a back reflection X-ray photograph as described earlier. The X-ray dislocation density D may then be found by using a relation due to Hirsch (14.4):

$$D = \frac{\alpha}{Bt} \qquad (14.1)$$

where B is the Burgers vector. For the observations on the (0001) face in ruby, discussed above, the mosaic misorientations observed were due to basal slip, for which system B has the value 4·75 Å. By comparison of the etch pit densities with X-ray dislocation densities Curtis showed that every etch pit on the (0001) faces examined corresponded to a single dislocation.

There are a number of more refined X-ray methods (e.g. Schulz, 14.5 and Birks and Grant, 14.6) more suitable either for the evaluation of a whole crystal face or for studies of specimens with relatively low dislocation densities (Lang, 14.7). As regards the former the general method is to illuminate a crystal face with an X-ray beam incident at the Bragg angle, Fig. 14.5, and to observe the intensity variations produced on a film which is placed parallel to the crystal face. As regards the latter those interested may read the original references.

14.2 Optical methods

In discussing optical methods of appraisal of crystalline quality (e.g. 14.8, 14.9) a major problem is that of laser crystals in which there is a requirement for optical quality which is not

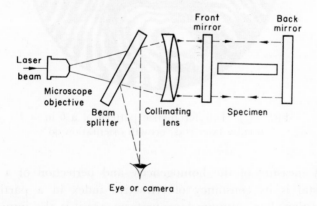

FIG. 14.6 A gas laser interferometer

necessarily present in specifications for maser materials. Chief among these optical quality requirements are the needs for uniformity of optical path length over different parts of the laser rod and for the scattering, which represents at best a larger than theoretical beam divergence or at worst energy lost completely from the system, to be a minimum. This Section outlines the principles of five of the more common appraisal methods. A more detailed investigation of the results which have been obtained by their use is given in the next Chapter.

FIG. 14.7 Interferometric pattern of a 6 in $\times$ $\frac{1}{2}$
in ruby laser rod (growth orientation 90°)

A measure of the homogeneity and perfection of a laser crystal is its constancy of refractive index in a particular direction. For optimum laser performance it is also important that the optical path legend should remain constant for all rays normal to the polished ends of the crystal. Interferometric methods are well suited for this as small changes in optical path length can be detected with high accuracy as fringe shifts. In these measurements the contribution to optical path length variation due to the dimensional and optical finish of the laser rod surfaces should be negligible. This condition leads to the requirements that the end faces should be flat to within one-tenth of a wavelength and parallel to within 3 seconds of arc. A diagram giving one arrangement for fringe formation is shown in Fig. 14.6. Here we can see a rather elegant use for a gas laser, namely as a high intensity source to enable better fringe visibility to be obtained with long laser rods. Fig. 14.7 reproduces the interferometric pattern obtained with a ruby rod 6 in long, and indicates how a 'contour map' showing path length variations is obtained. It is often convenient to evaluate the refractive index change per unit distance across the specimen diameter in terms of a figure of merit. This figure of merit F is defined as

$$F = \frac{\lambda}{2L} N \frac{1}{D} \qquad (14.2)$$

where λ is the wavelength of the light source, N the number of interference fringes and L and D the length and diameter of the laser rod respectively. In ruby F values of about 6×10^{-5} cm^{-1} are obtained with rather poor material and of about 1×10^{-5} cm^{-1} for good quality material.

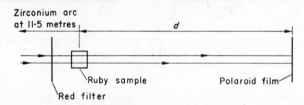

FIG. 14.8 Optical system required for producing shadowgraphs

A good deal of information, useful for quality control in growth processes, can be obtained from shadowgraphs and orthoscopic birefringence measurements. The optical system needed to produce shadowgraphs is quite simple and its essential parts are shown in Fig. 14.8. This method records on photographic film the shadow cast by a sample illuminated by light from a point source and gross non-uniformities of refractive index are readily observed. Fig. 14.9 shows a shadowgraph of a vapour phase ruby specimen. This shows spatial variations in intensity on the film resulting from angular light deviations localized in the specimen, occurring in this case in

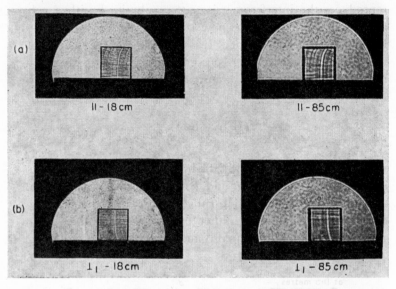

(a)

‖ - 18 cm   ‖ - 85 cm

(b)

⊥‖ - 18 cm   ⊥‖ - 85 cm

FIG. 14.9   Shadowgraphs of a ruby specimen; (a) parallel to optic axis, (b) perpendicular to optic axis

the form of linear striations. A development of the same principle is the birefringence viewer, Fig. 14.10, in which the specimen is viewed in polarized light. This again shows defects as intensity variations on the film (Fig. 14.11) — the regions of misorientation in the crystal giving rise to the light and dark patterns — but has the advantage that, since one of the polarizers can be rotated, estimates of relative misorientation may be made.

Another use of polarized light for appraisal is in the observation of optic axis figures. The optical system required to obtain these is shown in Fig. 14.12. The crystal is mounted in con-

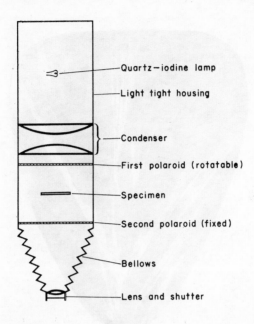

Quartz—iodine lamp

Light tight housing

Condenser

First polaroid (rotatable)

Specimen

Second polaroid (fixed)

Bellows

Lens and shutter

Plate holder

FIG. 14.10   Diagram of the birefringence viewer

vergent light between crossed polarizers with the optic axis along the line of sight. This is a useful technique for observing the uniformity of direction of the optic axis throughout the crystal because it is this which determines the symmetry of the isogyre pattern. Thus, if the optic axis of a crystal has different directions in different parts of the crystal the optic axis figure will become asymmetrical and confused. Where the isogyre

FIG. 14.11   Orthoscopic birefringence pattern
of a ruby slice showing defect structure
originating from the seed (crystal viewed
along the c-axis)

pattern is distorted but recognizable it is often possible to estimate the misorientation involved by comparison with patterns obtained from perfect material deliberately mis-aligned. Fig. 14.13 shows a set of isogyre patterns taken at five nominal positions over a ruby boule. We can see that there are some variations and in fact they correspond to misorientations of about half a degree.

Scattering experiments, in all of which defects such as inclusions, voids and dislocations cause angular deviation of a well-collimated light beam passing through the sample, form

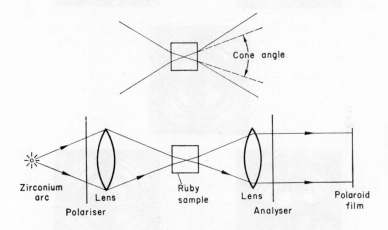

FIG. 14.12 Optical arrangement for observing optic axis figures

another class of optical appraisal methods. An arrangement for observing small angle scattering is shown in Fig. 14.14 where again a gas laser forms a convenient light source. Measurement of the size of the spot recorded on the film gives a measure of the angular deviations introduced and hence an estimate of the beam divergence that would be obtained if the specimen were used for a laser. An alternative method is to observe Tyndall-type scattering, in which a light beam is passed down the length of a specimen and observations are made in the plane normal to the incident beam.

FIG. 14.13 Optic axis figures at five different positions over a ruby specimen showing 'wander' of
c-axis orientation

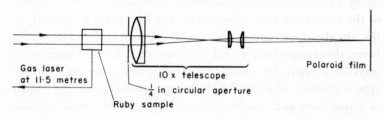

FIG. 14.14 Arrangement for study of small angle scattering

14.3 Electron spin resonance techniques

The use of microwave spectrometers in the appraisal of chemical constitution was discussed in Chapter 13 and the question now arises of the extent to which e.s.r. linewidth and spin-lattice relaxation time measurements can be used to provide textural information about laser and maser crystals. It is easy to draw three conclusions. Firstly, that in general the specimen size which can be accommodated in a microwave spectrometer cavity or waveguide assembly is small compared with the dimensions of typical laser rods. To this extent, therefore, microwave methods appear less attractive for the examination of large specimens (for example, completely fabricated laser rods) than some of the optical methods described earlier. Secondly, that the techniques for observing accurate lineshapes and relaxation processes are complex and the theory and interpretation may be difficult. Thirdly, and perhaps most important, that there are some crystal properties, such as variations in the crystalline electric field, the magnitude of mosaic misorientation and the amount of lattice strain, which are most appropriately studied by microwave spectroscopy simply because the environment of the paramagnetic ion has a great influence on the resonance signal. It is also evident in this context that it becomes increasingly difficult to separate and distinguish between chemical and textural influences because very often the effects observed are due to a combination of both. Thus, for example, if paramagnetic impurity atoms are present in a crystal we should not only expect separate resonance spectra from the impurities but also, depending on their nature and concentration, cross-relaxation effects which might alter radically the behaviour of the material at both optical and microwave frequencies. Again, if the radius of the impurity atom is very different from that of the metallic ion in the host lattice there can be intense local strains in the lattice. An extreme example of this occurs in the growth of iron doped alumina (Fe^{3+} in Al_2O_3) where it is very difficult to obtain large single crystals at concentrations higher than about 1% Fe without crazing. For these reasons measurements of spectroscopic parameters of the maser or laser material are very valuable in assessing the detailed perfection of the crystal. Since these same parameters are frequently those on which operation as a laser or maser depends we can see that there will be a close connection between crystalline quality and device performance. This theme is extended in the following Chapter.

References

14.1 THORP, J. S. and CURTIS, D. A.: *Quantum Electronics III* (Columbia University Press, 1964), p. 911.

14.2 CURTIS, D. A.: University of Durham, Thesis, 1964.

14.3 SCHEUPLEIN, R. and GIBBS, P.: *J. Amer. Ceram. Soc.*, 1960, **43**, p. 458.

14.4 HIRSCH, P. B.: *Progr. Metal Phys.*, 1956, **6**, p. 236.

14.5 SCHULZ, L. G.: *Trans. A.I.M.E.*, 1954, **200**, p. 1082.

14.6 BIRKS, L. S. and GRANT, B. K.: *NRL Report* 6087, 1964 (U.S. Naval Research Laboratory, Washington, D.C.).

14.7 LANG, A. R.: *Acta Cryst.*, 1959, **12**, p. 249.

14.8 BRADFORD, J. N., ECKARDT, R. C. and TUCKER, J. W.: *NRL Report* 6080, 1964 (U.S. Naval Research Laboratory, Washington, D.C.).

14.9 JACK, K. H. and STEPHENSON, G.: Unpublished communications.

* 15

Crystalline Quality and Device Performance

THE preceding two Chapters have considered some of the techniques available for estimating the quality of laser and maser crystals. In this Chapter a rather different point of view is adopted and the discussion centres on the relationship between device performance and crystalline perfection. In practice it may be found that a device fails to meet the required specification, or, in the extreme case, that it does not work at all. In such situations it is important to be able to select the most appropriate appraisal methods for studying the particular problem in hand. To illustrate these points two examples will be discussed. These are, firstly, the influence of different ionic states, and secondly, the effects of mosaic structure and strain. In neither of these topics is the situation as yet fully resolved but sufficient is known, at least in certain crystals, to enable some appreciation of the repercussions in both laser and maser operation to be obtained.

* 15.1 The influence of different ionic states

The first example concerns some features due to changes in the ionic state of the paramagnetic ion. As the development of ruby lasers proceeded there were reports that prolonged exposure to light from xenon flash tubes caused discoloration in ruby, which turned from the standard pink to orange, and that this change was accompanied by an increase in the threshold power required to produce stimulated emission. Almost concurrently it was found that during the growth of vapour phase ruby occasional specimens were orange coloured

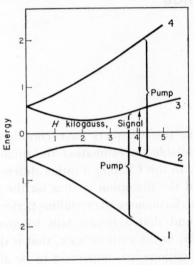

FIG. 15.1   Energy level scheme for inversion ratio measurements in orange ruby ($\theta = 54° 44'$, energy expressed in kMc/s)

and with these, contrary to the laser case, enhanced inversion ratios could under certain circumstances be obtained at microwave frequencies. These observations, among others, led to more general investigations of the causes and effects of the colour change which in ruby is now generally thought to be due either to changes in the ionic state of the chromium centres or to the formation of new centres by irradiation.

One of the first reports of resonance studies on natural orange ruby (grown by the vapour phase method) was made by Jolley and McLaughlan (15.1). In these experiments the specimen was mounted to suit the symmetrical double-pumping orientation shown in Fig. 15.1. The pump frequency was 23 kMc/s and the resulting inversion of the 2–3 transition was observed at 9 kMc/s. This inversion was then compared with that obtained from a pink ruby specimen of the same size and concentration (0·05% Cr) placed in the same microwave cavity. The results were expressed in terms of an inversion ratio I as defined as

$$I = \frac{\text{peak inversion}}{\text{peak absorption}} \qquad (15.1)$$

At 1·4°K the value of I was found to be 1·5 for pink ruby and about 5·0 for most of the orange ruby specimens examined.

The paramagnetic spectrum of the orange ruby showed the normal Cr^{3+} lines and also a broad line about 200 oersteds wide centred near $g = 2·0$ which was nearly isotropic with respect to the direction of the magnetic field. In the double-pumping position the broad line is coincident with the 4–3 and 2–1 idler transitions. Jolley and McLaughlan suggested that the reason for the enhanced emission from the orange ruby was that the broad line produced a rapid relaxation path between levels 4–3 and 2–1 by a process similar to that which is obtained by double doping with a fast relaxer, as in cerium gadolinium ethyl sulphate. The importance of the enhanced inversion ratio is of course that a lower pump power would be needed in an operational device.

The inversion measurements did not resolve the question of whether the additional line observed in the spectrum of orange ruby was due to the presence of ionic states of chromium other than Cr^{3+} or to some colour centre formed in this instance by unusual flame conditions in the vapour phase growth method. Subsequently a number of studies were made to find out more about the additional centres. The possibility of various ionic states of chromium existing in an aluminium oxide host lattice was investigated by Hoskins and Soffer (15.2), who carried out spin resonance and optical absorption measurements on single crystals of α-Al_2O_3 containing chromium which had been grown under conditions favouring the formation of Cr^{4+} rather than the usual Cr^{3+}. The crystals were grown by the Verneuil process, but a method of charge compensation was used to enable tetravalent chromium to be substituted for the trivalent aluminium. This was performed by including nitrides in the powder feed, which substituted some N^{3-} ions for O^{2-}, and subsequently maximizing the conversion of Cr^{3+} to Cr^{4+} by oxidizing the samples in oxygen at 1400°C for sixteen hours. The samples produced were a bright orange in colour.

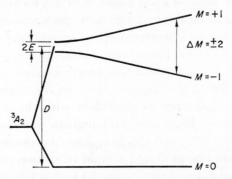

FIG. 15.2   Energy level diagram for Cr^{4+} in Al_2O_3

Some of the measurements made by Hoskins and Soffer will be described in detail because they form useful standards of comparison in discussing the effects of irradiation.

Spin resonance measurements were made with an X-band spectrometer. In addition to the normal spectra of Cr^{3+} an extra absorption line was observed at liquid helium temperatures at a magnetic field value consistent with the transition between the $M = \pm 1$ states shown in Fig. 15.2. In α-Al_2O_3 the trigonal symmetry of the field due to the slightly distorted octahedron of six oxygen ions leaves a ground state triplet lowest in energy. This is designated $^3A_2$ in Pryce and Runciman's notation (15.3) and is split, by spin-orbit interaction and the axial field, into a doublet and a singlet. The situation is similar to that of the isoelectronic V^{3+} in $\alpha\text{-}Al_2O_3$ on which spin resonance studies have been made by Zverev and Prokhorov (15.4) and by Lambe and Kikuchi (15.5). The $\Delta M = 2$ transition of Cr^{4+} in Al_2O_3 has a characteristic asymmetry evident from Fig. 15.3. The line is steep on the high field side

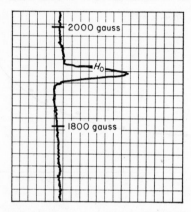

FIG. 15.3   First derivative presentation of the $\Delta M = \pm 2$ absorption line of Cr^{4+} in Al_2O_3 near $\theta = 0°$; (H_0 indicates the resonance value of field)

and has a long tail on the low field side. The form of the spin Hamiltonian is such that the separation between the $M = \pm 1$ levels is given to a good approximation by the simplified expression

$$h\nu = 2g_{\parallel}\beta H \cos \theta \qquad (15.2)$$

for measurements at X-band, where $h\nu$ is considerably less than the splitting D, whose value is 7 cm^{-1}. (The symbols in equation (15.2) have their customary meanings.) This gives a convenient method of checking whether Cr^{4+} is present by simply observing the angular dependence of the field H required for resonance. We can see from equation (15.2) that this will be given by

$$H = H_0 (\cos \theta)^{-1} \qquad (15.3)$$

277

where H_0 is the value of field for resonance at $\theta = 0°$. The close agreement between theory and experiment found by Hoskins and Soffer is shown in Fig. 15.4. Optical absorption measurements made on the same crystals at room temperature showed a large band with a maximum at 4600 Å, Fig. 15.5. It is this which gives the crystals their bright orange colouration. There

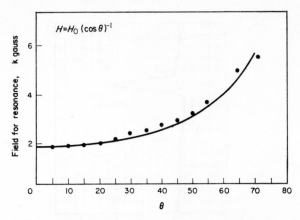

FIG. 15.4 The angular dependence of the resonance value of magnetic field for the $\Delta M = \pm 2$ transition of Cr^{4+} in Al_2O_3 (experimental points; full line, theory)

is a subsidiary peak near 3700 Å whose distinctiveness is enhanced when correction is made for the Cr^{3+} background in this wavelength region.

We are now in the position of having some fairly definite ideas as to the cause of the colouration in orange ruby. The next question is whether Cr^{4+} is a fast relaxer and, if so, to find whether its effect is generally detrimental or beneficial. The orange rubies, which occasionally result accidentally during attempts to grow pink rubies by the vapour phase process, have been shown by spin resonance and optical observations to contain Cr^{4+} as well as Cr^{3+}. The effect of the presence of Cr^{4+} on the relaxation rates of Cr^{3+} was studied by Standley and Vaughan (15.6) in orange ruby crystals which contained about

0·05% Cr^{3+} and one-hundredth of this amount of Cr^{4+}. Relaxation times were measured using a pulse saturation method at 9·27 Gc/s in the temperature range 1·6°K to 4·2°K. The relaxation behaviour of the Cr^{3+} ions was found to be very similar to that of pink vapour phase ruby. The angular dependence was consistent with Donoho's theoretical pre-

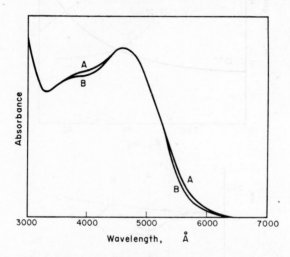

FIG. 15.5 Optical absorption spectrum of α-Al_2O_3 containing Cr^{4+}, σ polarization, room temperature; (a) before and (b) after correction for calculated Cr^{3+} background

dictions (15.7) and the temperature dependence was that of the direct process. This suggested that the presence of Cr^{4+} in the specimen did not appreciably modify the Cr^{3+} relaxation. This was confirmed by a series of measurements carried out in the regions where the Cr^{3+} and Cr^{4+} lines overlapped in an attempt to detect cross-relaxation between the two ions. Because harmonic cross-relaxation also occurred at polar angles near to the overlap positions a similar series of measurements was made as a control on pink vapour phase ruby of similar concentration in which the Cr^{4+} line was undetectable. One of the sets of results obtained is shown in Fig. 15.6. The

279

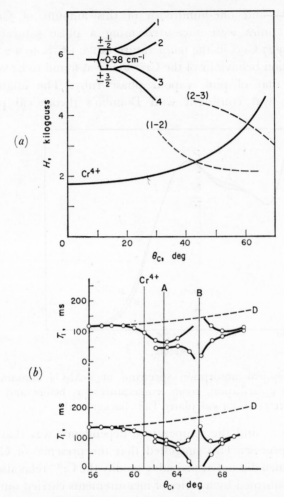

FIG. 15.6 (a) Isofrequency resonance chart showing crossing points of Cr^{3+} and Cr^{4+} lines. Full curve, Cr^{4+} line; broken curves, Cr^{3+} lines; with transitions as indicated

(b) Angular variation of relaxation times for the Cr^{3+} (2–3) transition at $4\cdot2°K$. The upper curve refers to the orange ruby, the lower to the pink ruby. The Donoho curve is shown as the broken line D. At the harmonic point A, $2\nu_{32} = 3\nu_{12}$; at B, $\nu_{23} = \nu_{34}$

similarity of behaviour between the pink and orange rubies is very striking and from the form of the curves we can see that in these specimens the harmonic cross-relaxation process was far more effective in altering the relaxation time than was cross-relaxation to neighbouring Cr^{4+} ions.

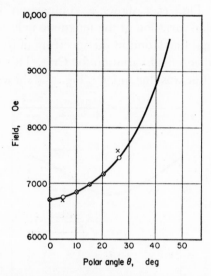

FIG. 15.7   Angular dependence of field for resonance of additional line observed in orange rubies (4·2°K). Open circles, natural orange ruby; crosses, x-irradiated pink ruby; solid line, predicted variation for Cr^{4+}

As stated in Chapter 3 the theoretical treatments of relaxation do not predict the strong concentration dependence found in early Verneuil ruby specimens by a number of workers. We recall too that concentration independent relaxation has been shown to occur in magnetically clean vapour phase ruby. One would expect that the concentration dependence would be due to the presence of a fast relaxing centre and the experiments just described show that this is unlikely to be Cr^{4+}. In ruby there is strong circumstantial evidence that fast relaxing centres are formed by Cr^{2+} ions. This evidence comes mainly from studies on γ-irradiated and x-irradiated pink ruby. After irradiation pink ruby shows an orange colouration which, on superficial visual inspection, appears very similar to the natural orange ruby we have been discussing. The similarity was confirmed by spin resonance experiments at 34·6 Gc/s (Mason and Thorp, 15.8). Fig. 15.7 shows a comparison between the observed angular variation of the magnetic field for resonance for the additional line found in the spectrum of irradiated pink ruby and the theoretical variation for Cr^{4+}. This suggests that the additional line was due to Cr^{4+}. Fig. 15.8 shows the effect of

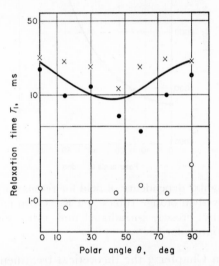

FIG. 15.8 Angular variation of Cr^{3+} relaxation in ruby at 4·2°K. Full circles, normal pink vapour phase ruby; open circles, after x-irradiation; crosses, after x- and U.V.-irradiation; solid line, theoretical variation (Donoho) scaled to fit at $\theta = 90°$

irradiation on the spin-lattice relaxation of the Cr^{3+} ions. X-irradiation causes a marked reduction in the relaxation times, but subsequent illumination of an x-irradiated specimen (which reduces the intensity of the orange colouration) increases the relaxation rates to the values they had before x-irradiation.

The most likely explanation for this is that x-irradiation converts some of the Cr^{3+} into Cr^{4+} and Cr^{2+} and that the Cr^{2+} ion is a fast relaxer.

So far the discussion has been concerned with effects in maser materials at microwave frequencies. However, differences in ionic state are equally important in laser materials at optical frequencies and a major difficulty in their growth is to ensure that the correct ionic state is present.

✳ 15.2 The influence of crystalline texture

✳ (a) Effects on maser performance

As we have already seen, synthetic laser and maser materials, although in substantially single crystal form, often show textural imperfections and mosaic structure to a degree largely dependent on their growth history. In all of these materials the presence of mosaic structure may lead to anisotropic broadening of electron spin resonance transitions, i.e. the width of a particular transition may alter as the polar angle between the crystalline axis and the d.c. magnetic field is changed. This is significant in connection with maser amplifiers because both the signal bandwidth and the pumping efficiency are influenced by the linewidth of the active maser material used. The measurements made by Curtis, Kirkby and Thorp (15.9) to establish the magnitude of the effect in ruby will be outlined briefly because they illustrate again the complementary use of two appraisal techniques, X-ray methods and spin resonance, to study a feature on which maser performance depends. In the first place we may notice that synthetic rubies grown by flame fusion from the vapour phase were used because these were known to be 'magnetically clean'. This meant that, since no lines except those due to Cr^{3+} in Al_2O_3 were observable in the parametric spectrum, the effects of interaction between Cr^{3+} centres and impurities were negligible and any changes in linewidth found could reasonably be attributed to textural differences. The textures of the specimens were examined by Laue back reflection methods, similar to those described in Chapter 13, and by making comparative observations at different positions on each specimen estimates of both the overall variation in c-axis orientation over the specimen and the average mosaic misorientation were obtained. The electron spin resonance measurements were made with a 35 kMc/s microwave spectrometer using a reflection technique, microwave bridge and phase sensitive detector. Several precautions were taken to ensure that true lineshapes were recorded and we will comment briefly on these as accurate recording of lineshapes is a very general problem in microwave spectroscopy. The d.c. magnetic field, which had been mapped in ancillary experiments by proton resonance techniques, was homogeneous over the volume of the specimen to 1 part in 5000. The detector crystals were operated in a region where the crystal characteristics were known, and the monitor signal power level was reduced to about 100 μW to avoid saturation of the transitions observed. As regards the auxiliary instrumentation needed for obtaining and recording the resonance signals, the amplitude of the high frequency modulation field was sufficiently small compared with the ruby linewidth to enable modulation distortion to be ignored. The d.c. magnetic field was swept slowly through the resonance value to avoid distortion due to the bandwidth of the recorder. Last, but by no means least, the filling factor η and operating temperature T were chosen as 0·01 and 77°K respectively so that the admixture of χ' (the real part of the susceptibility) into χ'' (the imaginary part) was reduced to negligible proportions. The derivatives of the absorption lines obtained from the phase sensitive detector and recorder gave, directly, the linewidth ΔH_{ms} between the points of maximum slope. Numerical integration of the derivative recordings gave the widths at half height, $\Delta H_{\frac{1}{2}}$.

By the use of X-ray and etching techniques two ruby specimens were selected which had almost identical values of *c*-axis wander and dislocation density but different values of mosaic misorientation. In the first specimen, A, the mosaic misorientation was 0° 30′ and in the second, B, a much more perfect crystal, the mosaic misorientation was only 0° 5′. The resonance measurements were of two kinds. The main experi-

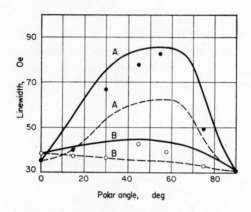

FIG. 15.9 Variation of linewidth with polar angle in ruby, $-\frac{1}{2}$ to $-\frac{3}{2}$ transition. (Full line, Lorentzian; broken line, Gaussian prediction; closed circle, specimen A; open circle, specimen B)

ment was to measure the values of $\Delta H_{\frac{1}{2}}$ for the transitions as a function of polar angle. In ancillary experiments the field values for resonance were noted as a function of polar angle for each transition so that, for reasons which we will give below, values of $\dfrac{dH}{d\theta}$ could be derived.

One of the sets of results obtained is shown in Fig. 15.9 which indicates that pronounced anisotropic broadening was obtained with the less perfect crystal, specimen A, and that the linewidth near $\theta = 45°$ was more than twice that of either $\theta = 0°$ or $\theta = 90°$. Some comment is necessary, however, in order to explain the comparison between the experimental points and the theoretical predictions shown in the Fig. 15.9.

285

The magnitude of the broadening ΔH due to angular misorientations in the lattice may be estimated from the relation

$$\Delta H = \frac{dH}{d\theta}\Delta\theta \qquad (15.4)$$

where $\frac{dH}{d\theta}$ is the rate of change with polar angle of the resonance value of magnetic field for the transition under investigation, and the parameter $\Delta\theta$ represents the distribution of c-axis directions produced by imperfections in the lattice. The crystal structure of the host lattice of the maser material plays

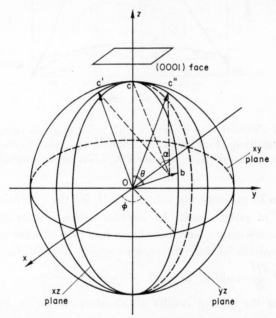

FIG. 15.10   Distribution of orientations in ruby

an important part in determining what the correct value for $\Delta\theta$ should be. Shaltiel and Low (15.10) showed that for a cubic material the correct value of $\Delta\theta$ was a parameter characterizing a Gaussian distribution of crystallite orientations about a rotation axis. This was assumed to cut off at a value corresponding to the maximum misorientation present in the crystal and agreement between the experimental and theoretically predicted line broadenings was obtained for gadolinium in thorium oxide, a cubic paramagnetic material. In ruby the situation is more complicated because we are dealing with a lattice having trigonal symmetry and we shall describe the position by reference to Fig. 15.10. Here the mean c-axis direction has been taken as the z-axis of the spherical coordinates. The basal slip dislocations form a set of rotation axes and we show one of these by b. The rotation axes cannot take up any position and in fact the possible directions of b are limited to regions within $70° \leqslant \theta \leqslant 80°$ and to $(\phi \pm 5°)$, $[120° + (\phi \pm 5°]$ and $[240 + (\phi \pm 5°)]$, where θ and ϕ are the angles shown in Fig. 15.10. (Scheuplein and Gibbs, 15.11.) In a mosaic crystal the mosaic blocks may be rotated about b by any angle up to a maximum, α, so that the c-axis can take up any direction in the region limited by c' and c''. When this is taken into consideration the distribution of c-axes when viewed along the z-axis is as shown in Fig. 15.11. The prismatic dislocations are distributed in a cone about the mean c-axis directions, but since this results only in an alteration in ϕ the e.s.r. spectrum, and hence the linewidth, is not affected.

The full lines in Fig. 15.9 are inserted because there is some difficulty in deriving the broadenings from the measured e.s.r. linewidths. In the particular instances of Gaussian or Lorentzian lineshapes it is possible to write, following Hughes and MacDonald (15.12),

$$H^2 = H_0{}^2 + \Delta H^2 \qquad (15.5)$$

and
$$H = H_0 + \Delta H \qquad (15.6)$$

respectively, where H is the observed linewidth, H_0 the basic linewidth and ΔH the broadening. In the experiments on ruby, however, the authors found that the lineshapes were neither Gaussian nor Lorentzian. The full lines in Fig. 15.9 are the predicted linewidth variations for Gaussian and Lorentzian lineshapes obtained by substituting the values of mosaic misorientation obtained from X-ray data for $\Delta\theta$ and using equations (15.4), (15.5) and (15.6). The experimental points

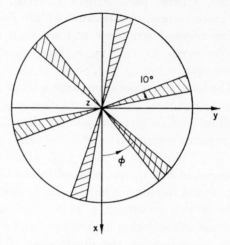

FIG. 15.11   The distribution of c-axis directions viewed along the z-axis

lie between these. The marked anisotropic broadening obtained with specimen A, whose mosaic misorientation was only half a degree, suggests also that linewidth observations could be used as sensitive indicators of this type of crystalline imperfection.

✳ (b) Effects on laser performance

As shown in Chapter 8, the beam from a solid state laser very seldom has the ideal uniform intensity over its cross-section and it is of great importance in improving growth techniques to correlate intensity variations in the beam with physical imperfections in the material. Fig. 15.12 gives an example of this type of correlation. This shows some integrated near field intensity patterns for two Verneuil ruby laser rods which were obtained by photographing one end of each ruby during oper-

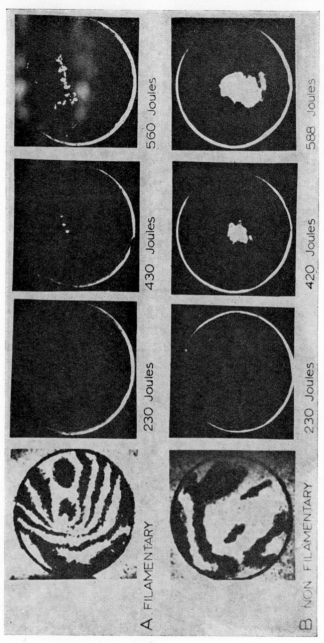

FIG. 15.12 Interferometric patterns of 2 in long × ¼ in diameter Verneuil ruby laser rods (90° orientation), together with near field patterns at increasing pump powers

ation. For each rod near field patterns were obtained at different levels of laser output by altering the energy supplied to the xenon flash tube pump source. The upper set of patterns, Fig. 15.12 (A), refer to a poor quality ruby and the lower, Fig. 15.12 (B), to a good quality ruby as judged by the Twyman–Green interferograms of the respective laser rods

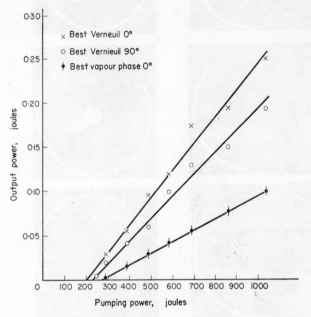

FIG. 15.13   Variation of laser power output with pumping power input for two Verneuil and one vapour-phase ruby rods

shown on the left of the near field patterns. The poor quality ruby gave a beam consisting of a series of intense spots which increased in both size and number as the pump power was increased. These correspond to the ends of emitting filaments along the length of the laser rod. The filaments appeared at the centre of the interference fringe pattern which here corresponded to the maximum optical path length in the laser rod. In contrast the patterns for the good quality laser rod showed that the output intensity spread our fairly evenly as the pump energy was increased. The superior optical quality of this rod is evident from the smaller number of fringes on the corresponding interferogram. A comprehensive set of measurements made to correlate refractive index variations with near field patterns has been described by Hercher (15.13).

Another problem concerns the question of the power output efficiency of laser rods. In ruby a considerable variation is found in laser output for crystals of the same size and concentration grown in different ways. The growth methods used in the production of Verneuil and vapour phase rubies have already been outlined in Chapter 12. Fig. 15.12 shows the variation of laser power output with pumping power input for two Verneuil and one vapour phase ruby laser rods. From this we see that these Verneuil rubies not only gave higher laser outputs but also have lower threshold powers than the vapour phase ruby rod. The explanation of these results is not yet clear. The vapour phase crystals are known to be at least as pure chemically as the Verneuil crystals and material grown in the 90° orientation is generally considerably more perfect than that grown in the 0° orientation (Curtis and Thorp, 15.14). However, the results of this comparison, in which the crystals used were selected as representative of the best in their class, show that the output performance may differ by at least a factor of two between crystals and demonstrates very clearly the need for comprehensive appraisal.

References

15.1 JOLLEY, D. G. and McLAUGHLAN, S. D.: *Nature*, 1963, **199**, pp. 898–899.

15.2 HOSKINS, R. H. and SOFFER, B. H.: *Phys. Rev.*, 1964, **133**, pp. 490–493.

15.3 PYRCE, M. H. L. and RUNCIMAN, W. A.: *Disc. Farad. Soc.*, 1958, **26**, p. 34.

15.4 ZVEREV, G. M. and PROKHOROV, A. M.: *Soviet Phys. JETP*, 1958, **7**, p. 707.

15.5 LAMBE, J. and KIKUCHI, C.: *Phys. Rev.*, 1960, **118**, p. 71.

15.6 STANDLEY, K. J. and VAUGHAN, R. A.: *Proc. Phys. Soc.*, 1965, **86**, p. 861.

15.7 DONOHO, P. L.: *Phys. Rev.* 133*A*, 1964, pp. 1080–1084.

15.8 MASON, D. R. and THORP, J. S.: *Proc. Phys. Soc.*, 1966, **87**, p. 49.

15.9 CURTIS, D. A., KIRKBY, C. J. and THORP, J. S.: *Brit. J. Appl. Phys.*, 1965, **16**, p. 1681.

15.10 SHALTIEL, D. and LOW, W.: *Phys. Rev.*, 1961, **124**, p. 1062.

15.11 SCHEUPLEIN, R. and GIBBS, R.: *Jour. Amer. Cer. Soc.*, 1960, **43**, p. 458.

15.12 HUGHES, D. C. and MACDONALD, D. K. C.: *Proc. Phys. Soc.*, 1961, **78**, p. 75.

15.13 HERCHER, M.: *Appl. Optics*, 1962, **1**, p. 665.

15.14 CURTIS, D. A. and THORP, J. S.: *B.J. Appl. Phys.*, 1965, **16**, p. 734.

16

Current Trends in Research and Development

In such a rapidly developing field as that of masers and lasers it is extraordinarily difficult to predict where the next advances will be because in many instances insufficient time has elapsed for critical appraisal of their possibilities and shortcomings. Certain aspects are, however, becoming apparent as centres for intensive research and development. This Chapter attempts to summarize the overall position, but for brevity's sake detailed descriptions are omitted. For convenience masers are considered before lasers, and for each class of device sections are devoted to characteristics of current designs, fundamental research and device development and applications. It may be pointed out straight away, however, that at the moment the preponderance of effort is being directed to lasers, laser applications and materials research.

16.1 Masers

(a) Features of current designs

The timing of the first successful operation of a maser was fortunate in the sense that it followed many years of study in

293

cryogenics, microwave electronics and electron spin resonance, the latter two of which had received great impetus in the post-war years following 1945. The objective, a low noise r.f. amplifier, had been evident to systems and communication engineers for a long time and the shortcomings of conventional vacuum tube amplifiers were well known. Thus the advent of the maser followed naturally when the knowledge and techniques in each of these three major contributory fields had advanced sufficiently. Furthermore, it was natural that the maser should then be applied — as in radio-astronomy and satellite communications — with little delay.

The present generation of masers, in particular the ruby travelling wave maser, gives the lowest effective noise temperature likely to be achieved in any amplifier. Indeed, as Chapter 6 shows, the limitation in practice is not the noise of the maser but that of the various components (e.g. the aerial, input leads and terminations) which comprise the essential parts of the receiving system. Even the TWM has, however, some disadvantages. The most important of these is the bandwidth limitation. This is now becoming insufficient to meet the increasing demands of communication system designers particularly in the field of satellite communication systems where bandwidths several times greater than those obtainable with present TWMs would be desirable. As explained in Chapter 4, the straightforward TWM already provides a substantial increase in bandwidth over the cavity maser, and indeed a fundamental physical limit is approached because the device bandwidth is nearly the whole of the linewidth of the e.s.r. transition used for the signal frequency. This linewidth cannot be greatly increased, for example by increasing the paramagnetic ion concentration, because this soon leads to the cross-relaxation regime where the effective spin-lattice relaxation times are so short that it is not possible, even with greatly increased pumping, to maintain adequate inversion ratios for maser operation. Attempts to achieve an artificial increase in linewidth by having a stepped magnetic field, or by fabricating a maser rod from several slightly misoriented pieces of ruby, have given some bandwidth improvement but still not sufficient to meet the demand.

Travelling wave masers also have, in common with their cavity counterparts, several other operational disadvantages particularly in connection with uses in satellites and spacecraft. All require a fairly large stable magnetic field (excepting zero field masers whose frequencies of operation are dependent on the material and often do not coincide with system requirements) and a low temperature refrigerant, usually liquid helium. Magnets, together with their supplies, add unwanted weight to the maser and one of the main drawbacks of the refrigerant is that it is consumable so that continuous operation over long periods may be precluded. (We may remember that amid the complexity of the Goonhilly receiving station it is still necessary to lift liquid helium manually to the maser periodically, a curious consequence of the low latent heat of liquid helium which has so far rendered it impossible to syphon the liquid over the distance from the ground to the maser.) Current research and development thus falls broadly into (1) fundamental research directed towards finding maser materials with better paramagnetic properties and (2) the investigation on the applications side of fields where the characteristics of present masers are adequate for making substantial improvements in some technique or control process. Before discussing these in detail, however, it should be mentioned that by no means the least of the maser's achievements is that, because its potentialities and limitations are reasonably clear, it has stimulated interest in other complementary devices, e.g. the parametric amplifier, and in a wide range of associated microwave and cryogenic equipment such as cooled isolators and circulators, miniature helium liquifiers and thermo-electric low temperature cryostats.

(b) Fundamental research

One of the most active areas of research on masers lies in the materials field. It is here that new discoveries must be made before any great changes in device operation are likely to occur. Zero field maser materials occupy a prominent position in this area. Sapphire, Fe^{3+} in Al_2O_3, is still the most promising of the few materials in which maser operation at or near zero magnetic field has been observed. The chief limitation of this material is of course that the frequencies of both signal and pump are determined by the energy level diagram of the material and often the signal frequency does not coincide with that required for an operational amplifier. Thus studies are in progress to find alternative materials suitable for different signal frequency ranges.

There is also an interest in materials with higher zero field splittings than ruby so that at a given signal frequency a lower magnetic field would be required. In this context chromium-doped spinels, beryl and rutile are still open possibilities as alternatives to ruby. Because of their higher splittings they are also more attractive than ruby as materials for millimetric masers. There are big problems, however, in the growth of these materials. Flux melt methods have been used to make doped spinels, but although small crystals have been successfully grown there seem to be limitations as regards the size attainable and the effects of inclusion of the flux. Here the next step appears to be trial of the Czochralski method of pulling from the melt. Beryl has in the past been grown in a very few laboratories by the hydrothermal method with limited success as regards crystal size, quality and purity. Equally rutile is not an easy material to grow in single crystal form largely because of the difficulty of obtaining the correct state of oxidation. If this is incorrect the spin-lattice relaxation time for the para-magnetic ion, e.g. Cr^{3+}, introduced into the lattice can be drastically reduced so that in a maser very poor inversion ratios would be obtained even with excessively high pumping powers.

The control of impurity content in maser crystals is also a region where much remains to be done. There are two major difficulties. The first is to eliminate unwanted paramagnetic impurities. This has been fairly successfully achieved in ruby. In other materials, however, improvements have not been so marked and the history of rutile illustrates the point. In the early years of maser development attempts to use chromium-doped rutile for millimetric masers were discontinued because of the high level of iron impurity in the crystals then available. After replanning experiments on the basis of using iron-doped rutile it was found that only by using 'pure undoped rutile' could a specimen with the correct Fe^{3+} concentration be obtained. Now, fortunately, better material is available. The second factor, which is one of concern in many maser crystals, is the presence of different ionic species of the required para-magnetic doping agent. Examples of this are the occurrence of Cr^{4+} and Cr^{2+} in chromium-doped specimens and possibly Fe^{2+} in crystals containing iron. Some of these ionic species are fast relaxers which would adversely effect the inversion ratios obtainable. The detection and identification of these centres is at present a matter of considerable difficulty with only micro-wave ultrasonic techniques and spin resonance methods offering promise of a solution. The control of the ionic state is essential for major progress on the materials side but advances are likely to be some time in appearing.

An associated region of active fundamental research, both experimental and theoretical, is that of spin-lattice relaxation. These studies are directed towards obtaining a better under-standing of the processes governing relaxation rates and hence, in device terms, attainable inversion ratios, pump power requirements and the feasibility of maser operation above helium temperatures. When it is remembered that even now the relaxation behaviour in ruby — by far the most used and

U

exhaustively studied maser material — has not been completely explained theoretically it is easy to appreciate the amount of work involved as these studies are extended to other materials in which the crystallography of the unit cell is not so straightforward.

(c) Device development and applications

The basic design features of maser amplifiers, both of the cavity and travelling wave variety, have been fairly well standardized at centimetric wavelengths. A considerable amount of attention is, however, being given to devising better microwave components suitable for helium temperature operation, to improvements in cryogenic facilities, to the design of more compact magnets with stabilized supplies and generally to the technological aspects of device construction.

At millimetric wavelengths, where demands from the communications, radar and radio-astronomy fields have been fewer, the position is more open. Numerous pumping schemes have been suggested and several pulsed and cw millimetric maser amplifiers have been operated under laboratory conditions. One of the difficulties encountered in this wavelength range is the small size of the cavity or slow wave structure whose optimum design may not be a scaled down version of the centimetric equivalent. A second problem is the fact that pumping valves at suitable frequencies are not so readily available, and a third that there is much more development work to be done before the performance of the necessary microwave components reaches that accepted as normal at longer wavelengths.

As regards applications it seems fairly certain that in fields such as satellite communications and radio-astronomy the maser will occupy a pre-eminent position as a low noise r.f. amplifier until it is superseded, if at all, by broader band devices with equally good noise properties. Extensions of the use of the maser are most likely to occur in areas where low noise is essential, but the bandwidth requirements are not so great as in communications. A field where these conditions often apply is microwave spectroscopy, particularly in the study of narrow lines. Here there is another feature which is very advantageous from the point of view of incorporating a maser. The low temperature facilities are very often a standard accompaniment in microwave resonance laboratories and so the maser's requirement for liquid helium does not present the same difficulty as it would for operational use outside the laboratory. Section 6.3 showed how the ammonia maser was used as an r.f. pre-amplifier for a 24 kMc/s spectrometer. The next stage is likely to be the development of solid state masers in a form suitable for use with the now fairly conventional microwave spectrometers. Here the wavelength range will certainly involve both centimetric and millimetric devices since increasing use is being made of the shorter wavelength spectrometer's additional versatility in studying materials with a high splitting (including some biological materials) and in providing greater separation in magnetic field between different transitions. It seems likely that in the next decade maser preamplifiers will become well-established components of microwave spectrometers. If this is so quite new possibilities will be opened up both for research and for the application of e.s.r. techniques to industrial process control.

16.2 Lasers

(a) Contemporary lasers

As earlier Chapters have shown, one of the most striking features of lasers is the large number of individual types to be found within the three broad classes of gaseous, solid state and semiconductor devices. This profusion provides laser sources at a very large number of wavelengths extending from about 3125 Å in the ultra-violet end of the spectrum to beyond 100 000 Å in the far infra-red. Although as yet the wavelength coverage over this range is not quite continuous, many of the gaps in the spectrum (i.e. points at which there is no direct laser emission) can be filled by harmonic generation using a fairly powerful laser source and a non-linear dielectric (for example, potassium di-hydrogen phosphate, KDP) as the harmonic generator. The common characteristics of the various types of laser are the coherency of the optical output, the intensity of the output as compared with conventional (pre-laser) optical sources and the small divergence of the laser beam. A special feature of the gas laser is the spectral purity of the emission which can be obtained.

There are, however, some very marked differences in the performance of different lasers apart from wavelength considerations. The first of these concerns the power level and waveform of the optical output. This feature is illustrated by comparison of the early helium–neon gas lasers, which gave power levels of about 5 milliwatts, but had the advantage of generating the emission continuously with ruby lasers whose outputs occurred in short pulses but which could, by the use of Q-switching, be made to exceed the megawatt level. A second difference, important from the applications point of view, lies in the wide variations in physical size between the various types of lasers. Thus the semiconductor laser is characteristically a small, lightweight device while the length of some of the more recent pulsed discharge long wavelength lasers may exceed several metres. These features are among those which determine the pattern of research and development on both lasers and their applications.

(b) *Laser research and development*

Some of the most active areas of research on lasers are those concerned with the provision of new laser materials (particularly in searching for those which will give laser emission lines at wavelengths corresponding to atmospheric windows), with increasing the optical power output levels attainable and with attempting to combine the most advantageous features of several lasers in a single device.

As regards the provision of new emission frequencies the problem becomes one of materials science exactly as was the case with masers. However, in laser materials the scope is wider and includes not only paramagnetic single crystals but also gases, gas mixtures and semiconductors. There is considerable activity in the growth and appraisal of laser single crystals, for example the tungstates, fluorides and garnets (particularly yttrium iron garnets and yttrium aluminium garnet) doped with rare-earth ions. Many of the problems familiar from maser crystal studies occur again in more pressing form because, for a laser single crystal, the optical quality is of paramount importance and in this respect the quality criteria are much more stringent than for maser crystals. In growth one of the chief problems is to reduce the strain in the crystal — in particular to obtain a more perfect local environment for the rare-earth ion — and attempts to apply the Czochralski method of controlled pulling from the melt are very much to the forefront. Detailed appraisal of these newer materials, including the garnets, is now being undertaken in conjunction with growth studies. Correspondingly there is active interest in the gas discharge field both as regards the energy level properties of different gases and gas mixtures and in connection with lifetime studies.

In addition to work on the provision of new materials for direct sources considerable attention is being given to harmonic generation. This is the optical equivalent of the technique well established for many years in the microwave region and has given rise to a new branch of research known as non-linear optics. This concerns the behaviour of dielectric materials interacting with intense coherent light and, in the context of harmonic generation, the conversion efficiency for each harmonic order and the maximum power handling capacity.

The trends in the search for higher powers can be illustrated by two examples which also show how research in related fields evolves. The first of these examples is the cw solid state laser. Recalling the normal ruby laser's operation the sequence of events is that an inverted population is established by illuminating the specimen with the output from a flash tube, that stimulated emission then occurs as a pulse of optical energy and that the ruby is then non-emitting until the flash tube can be re-energized. Thus the laser output is pulsed although very high peak powers can be obtained. Examination of this sequence shows that in principle there is no physical reason why continuous operation should not be possible provided that pump power could be supplied continuously. The latter requirement means that heavy duty discharge tubes are needed for continuous rather than pulsed operation, and several laboratories are engaged in this type of work. Although the flash tube is only a component of the complete laser, and much of its development is technological, some of the problems encountered are fundamental. Examples of these are the questions of life, gaseous clean-up and efficiency which are familiar from work on gas-filled valves and components such as TR and pre-TR cells in microwave duplexers. The problem of attaining cw operation is, however, not solved solely by the provision of a high-power cw pumping source. The laser crystal, subjected to a high, continuous power input, may rise excessively in temperature. Consequently there is the difficult problem of overcoming heat dissipation limitations in the crystal.

Another aspect of the search for high power is that of producing controlled pulses of laser emission. Here Q-switching techniques are involved and some of these are the subject of active investigation. There are again two aspects of this work. One is the development of switches which can handle extremely high powers with reasonable life. The other is the use of the properties of the Q-switch to control the waveform of the laser pulse and in particular to generate very short pulses. Liquid dyestuffs are among the materials being investigated in this connection and their photo-chemistry offers much scope for study.

(c) Laser applications

Some of the established fields of application of the laser have already been discussed in Chapter 11. These included ranging, optical radar, metrology, physics, chemistry and surgery. In all of these applications initial experiments have proved successful and further intensive work is proceeding. Both the pace and the results of some of this work are spectacular. As one example, the proposal referred to in Section 11.1 to use GaAs diode lasers for space-craft rendezvous control has been successfully put into practice. Both craft used pulsed GaAs lasers with which they could detect each other at a range of about 120 km. After the initial detection one laser system was switched off and the other was used to provide information on range and angle to the propulsion and attitude systems. When the range closed to 3 km a second GaAs system took over, providing range data to an accuracy of a few inches for the final docking operation. A second example of rapid extension of laser techniques may be taken from the medical field, or more exactly from dentistry, where it has now been shown possible to remove caries from teeth by laser methods rather similar to those used in eye surgery.

Several other new areas of application are awakening interest. One of these is the ring laser system used in rotation sensing. Here several lasers (usually gas lasers) are arranged in cyclic order using common reflecting mirrors so that independent clockwise and anticlockwise propagation paths can be maintained. Rotation introduces a differential change in the path length in the optical cavity and beats are formed between the clockwise and anticlockwise laser beams. The beat frequency is detected by a photomultiplier and measures the angular frequency of rotation of the system.

A recent example of the use of the laser as an analytical tool

303

is in plasma diagnostics where it complements established conventional optical and microwave techniques for estimating the electron density of the plasma. Lasers have also enabled the magnetic field in a plasma to be measured by utilizing the Faraday effect and plasma temperatures to be estimated from absorption measurements of the laser radiation. Though many of the diagnostic techniques have been developed previously the laser beam's intensity has greatly reduced the detection problem in this type of work and so is enabling the methods to be extended to much higher electron densities.

As the laser is an optical device it is perhaps not inappropriate to conclude this brief survey with a reference to laser holography which promises to become an extensive and important application. If a transparent object is illuminated by a beam of coherent light a small proportion is diffracted. The resulting beam contains the strong, coherent background produced by the primary wave which has passed round the object together with the secondary waves (with which the primary wave may interfere) caused by diffraction at the object. The pattern produced, which can be recorded on a film, is called a hologram. If the film is printed as another plate, or developed by reversal, the phase of the secondary wave determines the transmission at any point. Thus, if a beam from the original source is made to pass through the hologram a reconstruction of the object is apparent to an observer viewing the source through the hologram. Holograms of opaque objects can be taken by dividing the incident coherent beam so that half is scattered by reflection from the object before being recombined with the unscattered beam. The reconstruction of the object is three-dimensional and the coherency properties of lasers make them ideal sources for this type of photography. Though still in its early stages holography appears to be one of the many areas of science and technology in which the laser's influence will certainly be felt.

Books for Supplementary Reading

Cryogenics

Experimental Techniques in Low Temperature Physics by G. K. White (Oxford University Press).
Heat and Thermodynamics by J. K. Roberts (Blackie).

Microwave Electronics and Spectroscopy

Services Handbook of Radio, Volume V, by E. V. D. Glazier and H. R. Lamont (H.M.S.O.).
Spectroscopy at Radio and Microwave Frequencies by D. J. E. Ingram (Butterworth).

Optics

Fundamentals of Optics by F. A. Jenkins and H. E. White (McGraw-Hill).
Physical Optics by R. W. Wood (Macmillan).
Multiple Beam Interferometry of Surfaces and Films by S. Tolansky (Oxford).

Solid State Physics

Magnetism by L. F. Bates (Cambridge University Press).
The Electrical and Magnetic Properties of Solids by N. Cusack (Longmans).

Elements of Wave Mechanics by N. F. Mott (Cambridge University Press).
Semiconductors by D. A. Wright (Methuen).

X-ray Crystallography

X-ray Crystallography by R. W. James (Methuen).
Elements of X-ray Diffraction by B. D. Cullity (Addison-Wesley).

Some Physical Constants

Avogadro's number	$6 \cdot 024\,8 \times 10^{23}$ per gramme mole
Bohr magneton	
— electron	$0 \cdot 927\,3 \times 10^{-20}$ erg gauss^{-1}
— proton	$0 \cdot 505\,04 \times 10^{-23}$ erg gauss^{-1}
Boltzmann's constant	$1 \cdot 380\,4 \times 10^{16}$ erg deg^{-1}
Electron rest mass	$9 \cdot 108 \times 10^{-28}$ gm
Electronic charge	$-4 \cdot 80\,3 \times 10^{-10}$ e.s.u.
Electron charge per unit mass	$5 \cdot 273\,1 \times 10^{17}$ e.s.u. gm^{-1}
Planck's constant	$6 \cdot 625\,3 \times 10^{-27}$ erg s
$\hbar$	$1 \cdot 054\,45 \times 10^{-27}$ erg s
g value, electron	$2 \cdot 002\,29$
g value, proton	$5 \cdot 585\,5$
Ratio of proton to electron mass	$1836 \cdot 13$
Velocity of light	$2 \cdot 997\,923 \times 10^{10}$ cm s^{-1}
1 eV of energy	$= 11605 \cdot 9\,°K$
	$= 2 \cdot 418\,12 \times 10^{14}$ c/s
	$= 8065 \cdot 98$ cm^{-1}

Index